TAKE IT FROM EVE

TAKE IT
FROM EVE

by
EVE NELSON

Illustrated by Richard Rosenblum and Sheila Hanser

Grosset & Dunlap
PUBLISHERS / NEW YORK

DEDICATION

I dedicate this book to my husband, Warren Nelson, because he once said to me, "Honey, if you're so smart, why don't you write a book!"

CONTENTS

The Little Girl . . . *From infancy on . . . How to help your daughter to recognize and enjoy her femininity . . . How to develop her fashion sense, start good grooming habits, encourage poise* . . .The Teenager . . . *She's ten to fourteen, with all the preadolescent needs for sympathy, understanding, and guidance* . . .The Dating Years . . . *Beauty at college or on the job* . . .*The complete First-Aid Beauty Kit* . . .*Weekends away* . . . *Shopping for clothes and men* . . .The Young Married . . .*The turning point in beauty* . . . *Take the test: "Are you letting yourself go?"* . . . *Feel-pretty ideas . . . Get rid of the Drabs . . . Diet and the housewife blues* . . . Suddenly Alone Again . . .*The Young Widow or Divorcee . . . Can life really begin again at forty?* . . .*The NEW YOU* . . .The Young Grandmother . . . *Beauty Bank dividends . . . Six-point program for personal verve and lasting loveliness* . . .The Swinging Sixties . . . *How to approach the twilight years with the looks and spirit of eternal youth* . . .*Plus, "You're As Old As You Feel" quiz.*

Hairpieces and a whole new way of life . . . The facts about hairpieces . . . The seven major types of hairpieces, with illustrations . . . How to care for your hairpiece . . . Synthetics.

FOREWORD

by JEANNE SAKOL, author of *The Inept Seducer*

There are two reasons why every woman should read this book. First, it is totally engrossing entertainment and an earthy, straightforward philosophy of beauty. Second, it is different from any other beauty book you will ever read because it is written by a woman who has spent her life surrounded by men. It is written by Eve Nelson, a woman who believes that it's a man's world and that men come first in business and the home. "If God wanted it any other way, he'd have created Eve first."

The original Eve may have been the first woman, but Eve Nelson is the first woman to really tell it as it is. A truly contemporary Eve, she is a kind of ultra-female in the modern world. She knows what her job as a woman is and she does it with wit, wisdom, and exuberance that embrace everyone.

Unlike many successful women, Eve Nelson doesn't cling to her secrets. She has found a way to live and work and love and she wants to share that magic with all of us. Her advice is sound because it is based on reality. She understands the strengths and weaknesses of being a woman and she understands how to make the most of both.

Her energies and enthusiasms are boundless. In the frenzied world of advertising and merchandising, she is that rarity—a corporate vice president of a major merchandising chain, Spartans Industries, the parent firm of E. J. Korvette. One of the plum roles in the American business hierarchy for a man, it is that much more a tribute for a woman. She also heads the Eve Nelson Beauty Salons and beauty products. She is a true Gemini, adaptable, mobile, vivacious, witty, with interests all over the globe.

For Eve, life is a celebration. She pays attention to every minute in it. A perfect example of celebrating her own personal theory of life's adventures was her realization, at age 40, that she had never seen anything being born, and so she conceived a pre-Easter promotion for Korvette's Fifth Avenue windows to show chicks hatching out of their shells.

The best personal tribute to Eve is the fact that men worship her and women adore her. Blonde, green-eyed and bursting with a warm concern for others, she gives the same personal devotion and imagination to philanthropic groups as she showers on her oil executive husband, Warren, her family and friends and her career.

Closest to Eve's heart, among her many philanthropic interests, is WAIF, the organization founded by Eve's long-time friend, Jane Russell, for the welfare of war orphans. She heads the women's committee of Boys' Towns of Italy with Monsignor John Patrick Caroll-Abbing. She served as vice president of the Board of Governors for the Houston Council for Retarded Children and was the only woman awarded the Fellowship of the Institute for Retarded Children of the Shield of David in New York. As a successful woman of Italian descent, she received the American-Italian Awards (AMITA) committee Achievement Award for outstanding leadership in business. Her office wall is studded with honorary plaques for professional and charity accomplishments.

Eve's flair for communication was exhibited early — in her short stories and poems, written while she was an honor student at the Nardin Academy in Buffalo, New York. After attending the University of Buffalo, she started her career as a fashion copywriter, subsequently becoming divisional advertising manager of Macy's, New York. She then went to a chain of stores based in Houston, returning nine years ago to Korvette's as advertising vice president.

Her formula for success is simplicity itself. "Never stop being a woman." It may be a man's world, but women have a secret advantage. "Enchant a man's world by understanding and making him King—that's the formula, because then, and only then, does he end up making you his Queen." Of her husband whom she met in Texas and married in 1954, she says, "He's the one I lean on for major decisions and for love and approval of what I do." She possesses a "feminine" helplessness that endears her to the men on her staff and, in fact, adds to their respect for her executive instinct for what women want.

Take it from me. You'll read this book. Then you'll re-read it. Then, you'll give copies to your friends. To you, dear reader, and to women everywhere who want to enjoy life to its fullest —*Take It from Eve.*

TAKE IT FROM EVE

The Seven Stages of Beauty

To put it mildly, things have changed since Shakespeare wrote about the world as a stage and got all worked up about the seven ages of man. In Shakespeare's day, you were middle-aged at thirty, almost senile at fifty, if you lasted that long, and something of a social oddity if you lived to be a creaking sixty-plus.

Today, you can feel and be as young as your health and beauty permit. All of modern science from food and vitamin production to beauty and grooming aids are created to reach one goal: healthy, vigorous, attractive people.

To my mind, beauty for a woman begins at birth. You are a woman from the moment you are born. The Seven Stages of Beauty start right then—when the doctor spanks your fanny and says, "It's a girl!"

Each stage, as you will see, has its own beauty problems as well as compensations. Most women live simultaneously in several different stages of beauty, learning lessons from all to enrich and beautify their image. At the end of this chapter, you will find a quiz entitled "You're As Old As You Feel." Read the chapter first before you answer the questions.

The Little Girl

Maurice Chevalier sang "Thank heaven for little girls" and I couldn't agree more. If you are the mother of a girl baby or, like myself, are many times an aunt or godmother, or even a grandmother, you are in the enviable position of being responsible for the development of an utterly feminine and captivating creature.

It's up to you to create a female aura around her before she can even say "goo." Never mind that her tiny newborn eyes won't be able to see much more than shadows for the first month or so. Start at once to surround her with pretty colors —lovely yellows, lavendars, apple green, peach, as well as traditional pinks. Ribbons and ruffles and other "pretties" will not only subliminally impress her with the specialness of her own gender but will also influence the behavior and attitude of family and friends who hover around the cradle.

A tiny girl's personality begins to form at once. Her environment and the way she is treated by others will play a big part in how she eventually thinks of herself. While it's true that she can't actively appreciate a pink ribbon in a wisp of hair or a gay, flowered ruffle on her basinette, these things set the mood.

Instead of talking about the baby as "it" which so often happens, you'll be calling her "she." Visitors who see her feminine fripperies will respond and call her "she," crooning over her in honeyed words: "What a beautiful little daughter! . . . What a pretty little girl . . . !"

As every woman knows, flattery gets you somewhere. To be

told you are pretty goes a long way toward making you pretty. You can't start a moment too soon. During a little girl's first stage of beauty, until she is seven or eight, you are the Pygmalion who can develop a squealing red-faced blob into a poised, attractive young person.

Before she is even two years old and toddling, you can start your baby girl's beauty heritage by teaching her to take pleasure in being clean and smelling sweet and by keeping her hair neatly groomed. Most little ones enjoy the rituals of bathing, of being soothed and smoothed with baby oil or other creams, and of being dusted with powder.

Where the mother must make a special effort is in never allowing the baby to feel that these rituals are too much trouble. Babies are very sensitive to tensions and hostilities. Of course, you have a laundry to do and the beds to make and the table to set and a million other things, but think of your baby's training as an investment in her future. The adolescent girl who won't bathe or wash her hair, who neglects her body, is often one who feels she was "too much trouble" as a child.

It's *not* too much trouble to make bath-time a delight. Leave your exasperation in the living room and kick the couch if you have to. It's not too much trouble to get the special no-tears shampoo so that hair-washing doesn't degenerate into a festival of screams. It's not too much trouble to show baby the fun of little nailbrushes and washcloths which she will use later by rote, without a second thought.

Even before a tiny "she" begins to walk, the first man she makes a beeline for is her Daddy. Never mind any outsider's tight-mouth remarks about spoiling her or making her conceited. Encourage her to show off, to take pride in her new little pinafore or pretty shoes.

One of my favorite recollections is of my godchild, Eve, who was less than two years old when she rushed to the telephone to speak to her daddy. "I got new shoes!" she squealed with excitement. Then, with the exquisite logic of infancy, she held the receiver to her foot, shouting, "See! Aren't they pretty?"

My sisters used to give their little girls their own hand-me-down baby dresses for their dolls. The children took enormous pride in their cast-offs. They hung them up carefully and concocted all sorts of stylish combinations for the dolls. In this way, developing fashion sense got a practical workout at an early age.

As much as you love your little girl, don't allow love to blind you to her imperfections. Look at her clinically. See her as strangers will see her as she begins to attend children's parties, nursery school and the like. Spot trouble in the making and stop it before it becomes an established habit.

If she's a little butterball, it's adorable at three, less so at five and downright clutzy at six or seven with every chance of her being the butt of a nickname like "Butterball," "Beachball," or "Blimp." You surely don't want that. Eating habits and an attitude toward slimness must start early. A sudden, strict diet at age seven is a traumatic shock to a little girl.

Work with her hair. Make brushing a daily pleasure. Perhaps you both can brush your hair together, after her evening bath or just before she gets into bed. If she has curly hair, keep it short and well shaped. Nothing looks messier on a little girl than an unsightly tangle of wild, long hair. If she has straight but silky flyaway hair, give her bangs and cut the sides just below the ears for a neat, shiny cap. Use a dollop of hair cream or pomade to control the silky wisps. Very fine hair is almost impossible to contain in pigtails or braids, adorable as they may be. The cute, head-hugging cap-cut will always look neat and beguiling.

For the little one whose hair is very thin with no sign of filling out, consult your pediatrician. There may be a deficiency of some kind. Often, daily brushing with a soft-ish baby hairbrush will encourage growth.

One of the best gifts you can give your little girl is to devise a hair style that is both comfortable and neat. Teach her to use barrettes and rubber bands so she can do her own hair when you're not around.

Make any "problem" a source of pride rather than anguish: "My hair's so silky, I have to put beer on it!" "My Daddy loves me with short hair." "My Mommy and I brush our hair *together.*"

You must not allow her to become self-conscious about physical differences. Every time I hear a mother call her child "Freckle Face," or "Bugs Bunny" because of protruding teeth, I see red, green and purple! If she has freckles, she's going to hear plenty of comments on them. You must "adore" them, tell her how cute they are, and cut out magazine pictures of girls with freckles to show her.

Many a psychological wound has started to fester early for the little girl who springs up tall or needs orthodontia or has bright, carroty hair. It's up to you to create a layer of self-confidence so thick that the digs and jabs won't make much of a dent.

Your little girl is an extension of you. Take a look at the little-girl products available in stores. A cake of her own fairy-tale soap costs the same as ordinary bath soap and makes her bath more fun. Scented cologne, powders, brushes, combs and mirrors give her a taste for dressing-table magic she will keep with her always.

Have her at your side when you wash and iron her hair ribbons and her starched dresses. Let her "help" you hang up her clothes, fold her sweaters and jerseys neatly, line up her shoes, two by two, and straighten her toys.

For dress-up occasions such as a children's party, see that her party clothes are comfortable so she won't associate elegant occasions with misery. For your own cocktail parties, dress her up in her prettiest dress—including her baby pearls and bracelet—for her five-minute appearance before the assembled guests.

She will sense the electric atmosphere of a party and enjoy being the center of attention, if only for a moment. Here is where her training in poise begins. With gentle encouragement, you'll have her trilling "Goodnight, everybody!" completely at ease in a roomful of adults.

The few minutes it takes to dress her up are more than worth it. And if you're lucky, she won't spill anything on the dress and you can whip it off her real fast to hang it in the closet until the next special occasion.

The best illustration of this was told me by one of the executives of our Chicago store. It was the end of a busy, frantic day and he was supposed to drive his boss to the airport for an early evening flight. The flight was cancelled and so Our Hero said, "I live right near the airport. Why don't you come home with me and have some dinner?"

He called his wife with that five o'clock message that sends chills up the back: "Dear, guess what? I'm bringing the boss home for dinner!"

A half-hour later, the two men arrived. Who greeted them? The Brian's four-year-old daughter, dainty and adorable in a freshly starched, ruffled dress. The boss was captivated by his young hostess but her father was disturbed to see the table not yet set. Excusing himself to go into the kitchen, he asked why.

Mrs. Brian, as sparkling and shiny as their daughter in a pretty dress and fresh makeup said, "I thought it was better to spend the time making *us* pretty. Dinner's in the oven. I can set the table while you make the cocktails."

That little girl enjoyed being all dressed up and took her junior hostess responsibilities very seriously. The older man never had a more delightful time. Today, the ruffled toddler is twelve years old and well on her way to becoming a poised, vivacious, teenage model.

Although shopping with a child can be a chore, take her along for short romps through the clothes racks. Keep up a running fashion commentary that she will hear, mimic, and eventually understand: "This yellow pullover will go with your plaid skirt and your green corduroy snowsuit.

Your daughter's first stage of beauty is entirely in your hands. You are writer, producer, and director of the whole shebang. Benefitting from your loving care and experience, she will have a strong foundation from which to face the audience of the outside world.

The Teenager

Oh, that word! *Teenager*. As meanings of words change from use and abuse, the word *teenager* today is applied to everything from 4-H Club leaders to Haight-Ashbury hippies.

In terms of the seven stages of female beauty, today's teenager is nine or ten years old. She's not in her teens but she can't wait until she is. One of my jobs is to arrange fashion shows for teenagers. For the last couple of years, I have thought more and more frequently, "They look so young to me!" The only explanation I could think of was that they were looking younger because I was getting old—a thought that didn't do too much for my day, I can tell you. Then, I took a close look at those cute little faces behind the flapping bangs and crazy specs and I realized these "teenagers" were between ten and fourteen years of age.

Their older sisters, the actual fourteen-to-eighteen age group, don't like being called teenagers. "That's for kids!"

Parents of girls in their early teens are aware of this lowering of the age barrier. Problems arise when you think of your ten-year-old daughter as a teenager, because you may forget that she is only ten and expect her to behave and react like the teens you knew when you were one.

Your teeny may be clothes-happy for the latest miniskirts, vinyl coats, and purple tights. She may be causing you permanent ear damage by always playing her record collection at the highest volume possible. She may have teen magazines inside her geography book and her closet door is probably plastered with pictures of the Mamas and the Papas, photographs of the latest dances and the newest groups. The last holiday I went home, my twelve-year-old niece Carole had on her bedroom door a sign lettered in her most creative hand. "Keep out!" it warned.

Parents must not forget that all these are characteristics of preadolescence. Your daughter may be on the verge of or may have just achieved pubescence. Her knowledge about menstruation, her sophisticated comments about sex, babies, and LSD, or her passionate ardor for the young men of television and records may make you so nervous that you do forget that she is like many other ten-to-fourteen-year-olds.

She is a young girl. Social structures may change but the body and its beauty and health follow their own inexorable pattern. The young girl aged ten to fourteen is on the brink of womanhood. To put it mildly, she is often an emotional "wreck." Her body is changing rapidly; her glands are raising cain; she is riding a seesaw of extremes. One minute, she's way, way up in the air. Everything is wonderful. She's queen of the universe—a movie star, empress, and high-stepper. The next minute—bang! The seesaw hits the cement with a crash and her spirits crash with it. She's low-down and bruised by outrageous misfortune. Why? She probably doesn't know but if she does, she won't tell.

For the first time in her young life, she doesn't run to Mom. Being shut out of her daughter's life is rough on Mom but it's up to her to understand what's happening and to do her best to help her daughter through this period without moaning and groaning about being ignored.

In my family of seventeen brothers and sisters, I'm a kind of Auntie Mame to dozens of nieces and nephews. I've witnessed how the pre-teens hurt their mothers' feelings, ignoring them, and telling their troubles to their own friends or to an outside friend or relative, like me. It's fascinating to listen to these kids. The extroverts among them tell each other their innermost secret thoughts. The introverts are quiet, daydreaming about getting up the nerve to become extrovert.

The herd instinct is strong at this age. It takes five of them to dial a phone and ten of them crammed into one drugstore booth to decide on having the exact same thing. Panic is rampant over seemingly slight occurrences. A fad begins. The parents who will not permit their daughter to participate are asking for trouble.

If white baseball caps are being worn, let her wear a white baseball cap. If the girls are pasting stars on their arms or sewing bells on their skirts or wearing one blue sneaker with one red sneaker, why be the prune-face who says it's ridiculous? Of course, it's ridiculous, but she's going to do it anyway if that's what *everybody* is doing, so you might as well be her friendly "old lady" instead of the original witch-mother who makes it a horrible experience to go home.

This doesn't mean you should abdicate your role as Parent, nor should you lie down and let the kids walk all over you. An excellent expression of parental attitude was offered by the Nelson Rockefellers in discussing the raising of children.

"Freedom within a framework!" Rockefeller urged.

Happy agreed. "We try not to criticize our children for

12

things that don't really matter. If you save your criticism for important things, it's bound to fall on more receptive ears. What if a child doesn't want to wash his hands as often as you think is necessary? It's natural for children to rebel, . . . if you correct them too much, they react like flowers. They curl up."

To which I add, "Amen!"

At every stage of life, every human being needs to feel love and respect. A sense of personal dignity and value are essential. Without them, we are nothing to ourselves and can give nothing to anyone else.

Despite her shenanigans, your preadolescent daughter desperately needs your sympathy and constructive help. It's up to you to ferret out the problems she may be having and to anticipate those which may appear in the near future. This is a difficult time for mothers but a rewarding one when the results become apparent. A mother is comparable to a gifted sculptress working with human clay—the flesh-of-your-flesh. It can be pretty exciting.

By ferreting out your girl's problems, I mean looking below the surface. Try to be her friend and counselor even if she seems to be turning you away. She needs you.

If her hair hangs like a limp mop, if her nails are bitten clear up to the elbow, if her skin is beginning to pop out with blemishes, don't yell at her. Talk to her. The most chilling sight to me is the cruel exasperation of a mother. Sure, kids can drive you batty but they wouldn't be so obstreperous if they weren't hurting. Just as you eased the physical hurt of a bruised knee when they were younger, now you have to be a combination earth mother, movie star and delphic oracle.

If her hair looks rotten, talk to her about it. If it's the style you don't like but she likes, forget it. She'll wear what the other girls wear. If it turns out she "hates her hair," treat her to a styling—but at the hairdresser *she* wants or has heard about, not your old favorite. When helping her, do it on her terms, otherwise it's no good because you're doing it for *you*, not for her.

If her nails are bitten, don't be a nag about it. She isn't nibbling away with the express purpose of mutilating her hands. Help her to stop. Discuss it. Take her shopping to get some foul-tasting stuff to put on the nails. Offer an incentive for letting them grow beyond a certain point. Subsidize her to a weekly manicure to give her a goal. Ask her to choose a ring she would like. Either buy it or reserve it for the day her nails are nice enough for her to wear it.

A girl of about twelve who stopped to talk with me after one of our psychedelic fashion shows said her mother cured her of nail-biting with two tricks. "She made me wear white cotton gloves to bed that she tied on at the wrists so they wouldn't come off in my sleep. Can you imagine? I used to bite my nails in my sleep! And she bought me an enamel ring that I just loved! It took me two months to get my nails long enough. It's funny, but now the very thought of biting my nails is disgusting."

Skin problems often plague the young teenager. There are various reasons: the physical changes of adolescence cause increased activity in the sebaceous glands which especially affect the nose, chin and scalp. Pimples and blemishes on the forehead and on the back and shoulders are usually the result of "fallout" from the scalp.

At the first sign of trouble—maybe blackheads in that oily

area around the nose—don't make jokes; take action. Your daughter may whine, "Nobody loves me!" Don't take this personally. She desperately wants proof of love. Prove you love her by helping her to be pretty.

For mild skin breakouts, get her a supply of teenage beauty products. They are created by skin experts hired by the major cosmetics houses to meet the needs of young people. Medicated soaps and shampoos will clean her face and scalp and clear away oily patches. Other lotions and creams will increase her pride in her appearance.

Undoubtedly, your daughter reads magazines and watches television commercials aimed at her age group. Allow her to try the new products created for her. You may never have heard of them but she has. True, they may be offshoots of the same old stuff that you want her to use under a different name. Why make trouble? Let her use the new products packaged exclusively for her. Her enthusiasm for her own products will make her use them with more consistency—which is really the point, isn't it?

Ferreting out problems requires the instinct of a Scotland Yard detective. You may think her nose is pretty, although slightly large. It may not occur to you that she sees her nose as an enormous mountain unless you listen to her remarks. She may flee from a family snapshot, crying, "I can't have my picture taken—my nose is too big!" Or she may fuss and fret over her hair, sighing, "I can't wear that style—it makes my nose stick out."

Your daughter's worries about her nose most probably are unfounded. In fact, until she's thirteen, the size of her head may not yet have caught up with the size and shape of her nose. The worst thing you can do is pooh-pooh her dismay. She is not interested in the fact that you may have the identical nose or that a boy will love her for herself. Her nose is herself and if she is convinced it's wrecking her life, it may very well do just that if allowed to become a preoccupation.

Discussing things brings them into perspective. Tell her you see she's worried about her nose. Why not discuss it? Sit her in front of a three-way mirror and examine her profiles with her. What displeases her? Is the nose as bad as she thinks?

If your teenager is still convinced that her nose is an ugly mountain, explore the possibility of plastic surgery. If you say "absolutely no!" without investigating the possibilities, she will become more convinced that surgery is her only chance for happiness. Take her to a doctor. Let her hear his professional opinion—and you get an earful, too. As a rule, plastic surgeons will not do a nose job on anyone under sixteen because facial structure is still changing. Another reason for obtaining professional advice is this: the girl who seems obsessed with removing a barely discernible bump from her nose will usually have second thoughts after seeing a doctor and realizing this will mean an *operation!*

When fantasy becomes reality, it's a "whole other thing," as the kids say.

Teeth are another major part of health and beauty. Decayed teeth affect the health. Crooked, protruding or missing teeth can damage the developing adolescent personality. A broad smile is instinctive. If a girl is ashamed of her teeth, it is a crippling blow to her confidence as well as to her appearance.

Recently, at a friend's house, we were looking at an album of family snapshots. I noticed that in earlier photos my friend's little girl never smiled. In picture after picture, she screwed up her mouth in a strange kind of pout or simply kept it solemnly closed while everyone else grinned happily.

"How come Melinda never smiled?"

"Oh, that was before she had her teeth straightened." Melinda wore braces for two years and, as I could see a few pages later on in the album, she had a warm, radiant smile for her high school graduation picture.

The problems of tooth decay and crooked, protruding teeth can often be solved by orthodontia. It's shortsighted to think of braces as only having cosmetic value. Frequently, decay is caused by improper alignment of teeth. Upper and lower teeth crunch into each other at the wrong angle. Food gets wedged in the craziest places. Brushing and mouth wash go only so far. Braces not only can make the front teeth look prettier but also can save all the teeth from unnecessary decay and premature loss.

For obvious aesthetic reasons, braces can do wonders. A thirteen-year-old who wouldn't smile because she had a space between her top front teeth wore a simple wire retainer for six months that pulled the teeth together.

A friend of mine at the Westchester Country Club told me her daughter was a chronic victim of upset stomachs. Her parents were convinced it was nerves but an examination of her teeth disclosed she had malocclusion—her teeth didn't meet when she chewed. As a result, she had been swallowing food almost whole which affected her digestion, her skin, her energy—everything.

Above all, don't overlook your daughter's teeth. Don't dismiss her worries about them. Don't stint on professional help. Spend less on other things, if you have to. A new dress lasts a season; teeth are for life.

The teenager's diet is something I could write pages and pages about. It would make me feel good. It would make you feel good. But it wouldn't have the slightest impact on the teenagers themselves. You can't walk to school with them and wrench the pizza out of their hands and give them a nice lamb chop instead. You can't hover over them at the school cafeteria, leading them from the temptation of potato chips and pretzels to stewed apricots and leaf spinach.

All you can do is practice what you preach. Resist the urge to spoil them with a giant slab of your double-whip, extra-rich chocolate cream pie. Stop giving them second helpings of dessert. Go easy on the gravies, spices, and potatoes which make dumplings of your darlings.

If your daughter is overweight, don't say, "Remember your weight," and don't ask, "Why do you eat so much?" particularly when anyone is around. This approach alone is probably responsible for ten billion extra pounds put on yearly by young people around the country.

Once more, your help and sympathy are vital. Where the extra weight is between five to ten pounds, you can help her lose without outside help. Over twenty pounds suggests a deeper and perhaps psychological problem. Your regular doctor may help with a program of supervised diet pills and tests, or he may recommend seeing a psychologist for individual or group therapy.

Above all, don't you or your husband scoff humorously at "puppy fat" or predict it will disappear by the time she's eighteen. That's too long for her to wait. There are too many dances and dates, too many school corridors to walk through, too much suffering to live through in the meantime.

For the girl who is pudgy, start her on her weight loss by helping her to wear clothes that minimize her present bulges. This not only boosts her morale for now but shows her an immediate result of being a bit slimmer. There's nothing like incentive to keep you going.

Encourage her to report every minor triumph of will to you. How much better she'll feel about having a black iced coffee after school instead of a fudge sundae if she can brag about it to someone.

Daily weigh-ins on the bathroom scale will keep her mind on her goal. Protection from the rest of the family is important, too. Brothers can be especially cruel when teasing a plump sister. Talk to them privately and enlist their help.

I heard of one mother who put a lock on the refrigerator after dinner. "It was for my daughter's benefit. But now the whole family looks better—including me!"

The very, very thin child needs your loving attention, too. Often, the refusal to eat is a demand for love. Be sure you are differentiating between a "lean, slim little girl" and a scrawny skin-and-bones. I was one of those non-eaters, I remember. My problem wasn't a shortage of love but a shortage of time. I was so busy trying to be eight places at once that eating seemed a waste of precious time. How my family bribed me and begged me to eat! Then, I became a real teenager and the whole body cycle changed. I've been fighting the battle of the bulge ever since, wondering where those lovely days of slenderness have gone?

At ten or eleven, your daughter may be spending her first

weekends away from home, visiting a girl she met at camp or staying with relatives in another city. She may think she knows what to pack but it's up to you to remember things like underwear and the white slip that goes with the pink dress because otherwise she won't be able to wear the pink dress, right?

This is the age when she will be going to her first big dance. Don't wait until two minutes before it's time to leave to find out that she's supposed to wear white gloves or that she doesn't have a clean hankie in her evening bag—or, in fact, that she doesn't have an evening bag at all!

While I'm not suggesting you be the kind of mother who "does everything" (with the accompaniment of sobbing violins) for her daughter, I *am* suggesting you do everything to help your daughter learn to do everything for herself.

By being her best friend during these formative years, you pass an important milestone on the road to being grown-up friends in later years. As girls reach fifteen and sixteen, they can teach their mothers a few things—if Mom will listen!

For your own sake, listen when she says, "Mom . . . you're not going to wear that dress!" or "Mom, let *me* fix your hair."

It's a thrilling moment when the tables turn and the adult learns from the teenager. Relax and enjoy it for it's inevitable, but don't despair, you'll get a second time around when she has a few daughters.

The Dating Years

Whether you're at college or already on the job, the kid stuff is over. The herd is disbanded. You may be anywhere from eighteen to twenty-six, but for single girls this stage of beauty is one of emerging individuality. This is the time when you stop looking like a million other girls and achieve your own distinctive character.

This is probably the most romantic time of your life. Anything can happen, any hour of the day or night. You know you should look great all the time because who knows *who* will walk into your office or lecture class and stay to ask you for a date. Who knows *what* is waiting on the other side of the door when your roommate's date brings an extra man for you.

To borrow a motto from the Boy Scouts, the best personal creed is: "Be Prepared."

Every office has a First-Aid kit. The wise girl keeps a first-aid beauty kit in her bottom desk drawer or in back of the filing cabinet. It's a good investment to keep accessible an extra set of essential products and beauty aids. The value of this kit was indelibly engraved on my mind by Carol Duffy, my secretary, when she first came to work for me. She was single, as were many of the copywriters and artists in my department. More than once her desk drawer "Beauty Parlor" saved our skins (literally!). I don't dare tell you how many times I had to borrow things until I launched the Eve Nelson products. Today, of course, my office is fully stocked with cosmetics, creams, and wigs—and my staff borrows from me.

A personal survey of attractive young career girls revealed the following items as necessary for nine-to-five beauty emergencies as well as for the last-minute date right after work.

First-Aid Beauty Kit:

Nails: Emery board, nail polish, polish remover
Hair: Hairbrush, comb, hair spray

Face: Face cleanser pads, makeup base, basic eye makeup
  such as liner, shadow, mascara, an extra lipstick.
Other useful items include: Tissues, cotton-tipped sticks.
Your favorite perfume or cologne. Personal emergency items
which you know from experience are things you're always
running out of or need at the last minute. One girl said
stockings, another said aspirin, and a third suggested tam-
pons. Several mentioned a fold-up umbrella—"Every time
I have a last-minute date, it rains!"

At this stage of your beauty life, you must crystalize your
personal image and get rid of whatever doesn't suit the picture you want to have of yourself. There are practical aspects
to guide you.

A sexy hairdo that gets in your eyes may be very fetching
indeed but it's going to put a crimp in your work—unless you
happen to own a seeing-eye dog who can type. Comfort
counts for a lot during the eight working hours. Hair styles
and fashions change frequently and you'll probably want to
change with them. The trick is to choose variations on the
latest style that allow you to sit for hours, move your arms
freely without binding, and look fresh and unrumpled at quit-
ting time.

Select fabrics that will "sit" without crushing in the back or
folding into deep creases in front. Choose styles that are current and fun, yes, but which are restrained enough to merit
confidence from your superiors. Save the existentialist gear
for evenings and weekends.

Find a becoming hairstyle that will stay put all day. I can't
overemphasize the importance of this simple rule. Short, neat
hair looks great by day and can change into Alice-in-Wonder-

land at night when you add a long, silky fall. (See the chapter on wigs.) Long hair looks great by day, too—but not hanging around your shoulders like Ophelia on her way to the lily pond. Tie it back with a velvet ribbon or a silk scarf. Otherwise, it might get caught in the electric typewriter and short-circuit the whole building. . . .

Since you never know which Prince Charming is going to come through what glass door, you should strive toward a visual image on the job that becomes second nature to you.

If you wear glasses at work, be sure the frames are becoming. If you work in a typing pool or at a desk in view of lots of people, think about how you must appear from various angles. Consciously improve your posture. Sitting straight will make you feel less tired in addition to looking better. Be sure the top half of your body is attractively but fully covered. Don't let bra straps show or wear a slippery blouse that keeps coming untucked from the skirt. Show off your figure subtly. Save the crochet dress and body stocking for the discotheque. It may make some friends at the office but it's sure to make enemies among the big brass.

Elsewhere in this book (pp. 97-101), Mister Antoine M., who is the creative director of the Eve Nelson Beauty Salons, gives some valuable points about hairstyling and individuality. In direct relation to the career-girl stage of beauty, he advises you to wear one of your favorite outfits when you first go to a hair stylist.

"How else can the stylist see the entire picture of you? He can't tell what you look like from your face alone."

This is especially sound advice when you are searching for a completely individual "total look" for yourself. On a vacation trip to Palm Beach, I was interviewed for the women's page of *The Miami Herald*. The reporter asked what I thought of the miniskirt.

I said, "There's no such thing as a miniskirt. It should be called The Mini Look, a total look that includes shoes, hosiery, jewelry, hairdo. A miniskirt without the rest is like a ship without a sail. It can't go-go anywhere!"

With the aid of hairpieces, you can wear your hair many different ways but always coordinate the flavor of your hairstyle with the flavor of your clothes. In other words, an elaborately styled wig is magnificent for the charity ball on Saturday night. It's a bit jarring the next day for an afternoon stroll in a pants suit.

Weekends play an important part in the dating (and husband-baiting and mating) game. There are summer jaunts to beach houses and mountain lodges, winter ski trips, long-distance hauls for a football game or a friend's wedding—or simply because somebody said, "Let's go!"

While the exact permutations of clothes and accessories could fill a whole book, my personal motto for weekends is: "Count on nobody and nothing!"

Always take a good, big mirror, extra combs, bobby pins, safety pins, small scissors, emery board and adhesive bandages. I never need a bandage at home but I always need one during a weekend. Also, take a small but strong flashlight. Beach houses and ski huts always have three-watt bulbs which can result in your sticking your false lashes on your ear.

Whatever you have to leave out, include in a hairpiece or other quick-switch hair beautification. The rush and tumble of weekends may go to your head in more ways than one but to avoid the sudden desire to commit suicide Saturday night after a day with nature, be prepared to cover nature's mistakes.

As for your wardrobe and the tedious problems of being well-dressed on a budget, the soundest words on this subject were spoken by a junior executive at a television station: "Set your own standards of importance," she said. "If you love shoes, then have lots of shoes and wear them with fewer dresses or suits. The same thing applies to bags or hats or sweaters."

Sandra, another niece of mine, lives by this rule. When she was a Senior at Bucknell she splurged on a fur coat. She loved it and made do with a few very inexpensive shifts and some coordinated skirts and tops. She also had only an alligator bag on her Christmas list. She really wanted it so she got it—and it was worth having fewer cocktail dresses in order to have that super-duper bag over her arm.

To me a good way to shop is ask yourself two questions:
• Do I really need it?
• Do I really love it?
If you can answer "Yes" to both, go to it, baby!

The career or college girl who rushes into marriage because everyone else is doing it often finds that getting there is all the fun! Courtship, engagement, and the flurry of plans for a wedding are a form of heady stardom. It's irresistible to say "I do"—even if you don't, or even if you don't *exactly* know for sure whether you want to add a hot stove to your already humming electric typewriter.

The two questions become:
• Do I really need him?

• Do I really love him?

In irreverence there is often a refreshing truth. In his *Devil's Dictionary*, essayist Ambrose Bierce wrote of a couple about to be married:

> They stood before the altar and supplied
> The fire themselves in which their fat was fried.

Remember, the more you enjoy your life as a single girl, the more you will bring to marriage. Regrets are most often based on the things you didn't do, the places you didn't see, rather than on the bloopers you committed.

So play one of Frank Sinatra's old records over again and "Take It Nice and Easy." But not too easy!

A girl who used to work for me went to the opposite extreme. She was the prima donna who turned down dates without giving the man half a chance because she was waiting for Prince Charming. She was waiting for a man who was handsome, rich, brilliant, witty, successful, and sexy. And for all I know, she may still be waiting!

The Young Married

This is the turning point in a woman's beauty life. You have one or two babies. Your husband is fighting for advancement in his career or business. You feel like a circus juggler who can never slow down or stop moving.

Small children make incessant demands on the young wife's time and energy. Money problems pile up as you struggle to provide tempting meals and a cozy atmosphere for your husband while keeping up with the shoes, doctors' bills, nursery school, and the other enormous expenses associated with such tiny children. Your husband's financial success may be slower in coming than you both hoped and his frustration is yet another demand on your emotional and physical health.

As I said above, this is the critical turning point. Besieged from all sides by family and responsibility and tired most of the time, you must either make a decisive jump forward as an individual, or start slipping backward into drab facelessness.

Unfortunate but generally true, the young married woman who lets herself slip backward can rarely stop the downward trek to oblivion. It's like a landslide. There's a point at which it can be stopped. After that—watch out.

Are You Letting Yourself Go? Take this test, answering *yes* or *no* to the following:

1. Do you blame your lumpy-dump figure on your last baby?
2. Are you "too busy" to go to the hairdresser?
3. Do you wear old dresses or your husband's worn shirts around the house, excusing yourself by saying, "Who sees me?"
4. Is your hair worn in an unflattering style because "it's easier?"
5. Was the last time you wore eye makeup New Year's Eve?
6. Does a sudden invitation to join your husband for a business dinner or cocktail party throw you into a state of panic because you don't know "what they're wearing?"
7. Do your fingernails look as if you've been digging ditches without a shovel?

8. Have you noticed that your husband doesn't have much of a sense of humor anymore?
9. And that he "forgets" to kiss you goodbye most mornings?
10. And this year, he didn't remember your birthday?

If you answered *yes* to five or more of these questions, you are not only letting yourself go to pieces but your marriage as well. Tighten your grip, but quick, or the rope may slip clear through your fingers before you realize it—leaving you holding on to nothing.

Five years from now, don't be asking, "Where did it all go?" I didn't marry until I was thirty-one and I vowed then to increase my vigilance about my appearance. The worst thing you can say to yourself is "I've got a husband, now I can relax."

How to Feel Pretty Although Busy

The wife-mother-homemaker-nurse-accountant-electrician-carpenter-cook-laundress puts in a twenty-hour day. It's no joke but it can be an exhilarating, gratifying challenge—if you look and feel pretty.

Obviously, you have to simplify your beauty rituals. I'm certainly not suggesting you spend the day at a beauty salon. Feeling and looking pretty are a matter of planning and perspective.

Here are some practical suggestions for Young Married beauty:

Feel-pretty Ideas

CASE I   One of the executives in our Detroit store told me the only makeup his wife wears at home is false lashes.

"She says they make her feel dressed—and wide-awake, too!" he explained. "She's become so adept at wearing them, it takes two minutes to put them on first thing in the morning. She wears her hair in a sleek ponytail for housework, adds a cluster of wiglet curls for going-out nights."

"It's quick—and I feel fabulous!" she subsequently explained when we met.

CASE II   I asked a perky Darien, Connecticut, mother of two teenagers her beauty secret.

"Get rid of the drabs. Look good for your own sake!" she said. She wears colorful drip-dry culottes for housework, marketing, and painting in her studio. For cold weather, she wears patterned tights, high boots, and bright, comfortable outer wear that keep her cheerful and toasty warm whatever her activities.

"If I make the effort to look pretty, my children respond. My husband responds. Even the butcher at the supermarket brightens up and throws in some bones for the dog."

CASE III   "Housewife Blues start with poor diet!" announced my niece, Marlene Pedini, who describes herself as "an old married lady of twenty-eight."

"I'm worried about getting fat so I skip breakfast. Then, about eleven, I think I'm going to die so I have a doughnut and some chocolate milk for energy. Then I feel guilty about all those calories, so I skip lunch. Three o'clock, it's too late to have lunch even though I'm starved so I have a cookie or a coke with the children to keep me going."

No wonder that every time she gets on the scale she's aghast and discouraged.

CASE IV From an active young mother in Salamanca, New York, come these words: "My favorite way to feel pretty? Perfume! I love to smell glamorous. To me, a spray of cologne over my bare neck and shoulders when I'm getting dressed is like a brisk mountain stream. I keep scent in the kitchen, a pocket-size bottle in the glove compartment, and purse fla-cons in my handbag or evening bag. Fragrance has become second nature to me. The alcohol stings my skin. The essence assails my nostrils. I'm ready to fly!"

After a stretch of housework or cooking, she pours some cologne in her hands, rubs each arm and then gently presses the palms of her hand across her forehead and temples.

"It eases tensions in half a second."

CASE V My niece, Angela, is two years younger than I. She has *ten* children. Far from being a wreck, she has worked out the perfect formula for running a household that on weekends involves thirty-six meals a day. Angela beds down her brood Army-style in bunk beds with separate drawers, shelves and hooks marked for each child. The younger ones get the lowest shelves, of course, and each child is responsible for his or her own bed and belongings.

Breakfast is served cafeteria style. The children move along a serving counter, taking their own fruit, cereal, eggs, milk, bread. They sit around a huge table. When finished, they scrape their plates and put their dishes into the dishwasher.

Angela designed the floor plan of her laundry room to achieve the same efficiency. At the end of the day, the children take their soiled clothes to the laundry room. Underwear goes on one pile, colored items on another, dry-cleaning on a third for Mom to take to the cleaner's.

As happens in many big families, the older children naturally assume responsibility for the younger. They are encouraged to share and settle their differences between themselves. Angela's husband is happy. Angela herself looks beautiful and seems to have time for everything!

At the risk of being a Pollyanna, I have a simple message for the overwrought Young Married who feels that all she has left in life is a mountain of laundry, a mountain of dishes, and a mountain of bills. My message is: Simplify, select and enjoy.

Simplify routines as my niece, Angela, did. By this I don't mean sacrifice, as would be the case if you consistently served frozen TV dinners or canned beans for dinner. That would be simple, sure, but it would be gypping your family of nourishing food.

Simplify regular chores by doing them the same way each time using the same equipment stored in the same place. Become your own efficiency expert. How can you make life easier for yourself? Would a pegboard wall with hooks help you to organize equipment? If so, get one. Have you ever figured out why you really hate to dust? Maybe because the dust gets in your hair. Why not get a pretty cap to wear while cleaning? This is also a great time to cream your face. The creamy lotion will moisturize and smooth your skin and at the same time protect it from particles of dust and grime. When you put the duster away, all you do is wash your face.

Select the wifely duties for which you have time and talent. Too many Young Marrieds feel compelled to jump into everything at once. If you're serving on five committees, learning to bottle fruit, refinish furniture, make the children's clothes and speak French three afternoons a week, no wonder you're haggard.

In your zeal to be an active member of the community, remember that charity begins at home. If you can't run a literary tea and get home in time to present a beautiful picture presiding over a beautiful table, forget the tea party.

Enjoy to the fullest the time spent with your husband and children. Don't hold back. You have a million things to do? So does everyone else! The ironing can wait. What do you want to remember in your old age, the happy hours you spent ironing—or the happy hours spent doing a jigsaw puzzle with the family or taking a ride or just sitting around the family room, talking?

"A penny saved is a penny earned" is more than a monetary proverb for the Young Married. Saving for that eventual rainy day need not be limited to cold cash. Saving also means taking care of your skin and hair and figure now so they will take care of you in later years. It means getting enough sleep, exercise and nourishing food during the childbearing years so you won't look like a worn-out baby machine once that function is complete. It's continually developing your own personality and intellect so that you, the young bride who looks and acts like hundreds of other pretty newlyweds, will emerge as an exciting, distinctive individual.

What you do now is your money in the bank, in effect, your Glad Money, a fund of accumulating treasure you'll draw upon as the years go on. Believe me, this kind of wealth is better than an annuity.

Suddenly Alone Again

Being divorced or widowed in your middle years is comparable to being reborn—with all the innocence and vulnerability of the untried but, unfortunately, with all the wear and tear of the years in full view.

I would not presume to suggest that the changeover from being married to being single is a fun-filled frolic. Whatever the circumstances, it's a shock to a woman's nervous system and a harsh confrontation with reality.

"I've been a wife for so long. How do I go back to being a woman?"

The best solution is to meet change with change.

This isn't as capricious as it may sound. You may have looked fine as the woman you were . . . but you are not that woman anymore. You are by circumstance a different woman now. You may be hurt, bruised, used, exhausted, sad, and maybe secretly relieved that the divorce or the hideous illness is over.

Where does that leave you? A lonesome onesome of a twosome that isn't.

Finding yourself suddenly alone is a scary experience for women who have been married for a long time. In the song, "There'll Be Some Changes Made," Sophie Tucker sang "Nobody loves you when you're old and gray." This thought must occur to every woman who looks at herself in the mirror and moans, "What am I going to *do*?"

Plenty!

This is one time in your life to concentrate on yourself. Make changes in your appearance, your wardrobe, your daily activities.

Listen to advice, sure, but obey only your own instincts and desires. When a woman is suddenly alone, all the world knows "what's best" for her. Pay attention, yes, but remember that it is your life, not theirs.

It may not occur to you for a while, but you are now a free agent. You may not like the idea but, suddenly, your freedom to do and go as you please makes you a threat to the rituals and restrictions of other people's lives. That makes them nervous. You may actually do something exciting that they can't do. So they advise you to take up tatting or live with the children or move in with another widow-lady and spend the evenings quietly playing gin rummy.

I remember a movie on the Late Show in which Jane Wyman played a widowed mother of teenage children. She wanted to marry Rock Hudson (wow), but her children and neighbors talked her out of it. The children needed her. How could she desert them? She broke off with Rock (sigh) and was devoting her lavender years to becoming the family saint, when what happens? The children leave home and buy Mom a TV set to keep her amused during the cold winter nights! Fortunately, Rock was still hanging around.

This rather sudsy aside nevertheless has a kernel of truth at its core. Nobody knows what's best for you except Y-O-U and YOU may have to do some digging to find out.

Entire books are written for the divorcee or widow. Here, I shall limit myself to a discussion of beauty and grooming and the social and personal attitudes involved.

When you've been through hell, the best medicine you can

have is to be told: "I didn't recognize you. You look ten years younger!" The best way to achieve this is through change.

You've never dyed your hair? Okay. Dye it now. Hair-coloring is quick, safe and socially acceptable. You've always wanted to be a blonde? What's stopping you? You've secretly hankered to try bangs or streaks or to simply turn yourself over to a stylist, close your eyes and be transformed? Go ahead. There's no reason for you not to make whatever beauty changes you want.

Don't ask friends or family for advice. The jazzier ones may urge you to go ahead. Usually, however, you can count on shaking heads and mournful warnings about your age or that you'll look silly.

If you look silly, there's no rule that says you have to keep looking silly. The beauty parlor door works both ways.

You can be anything you want to be.

Do blondes have more fun? Try it and find out.

Is middle-age spread threatening to spread even further? Sign up for an exercise class. Join the "Y." Examine the various diets and find one you can stick to. Instead of "being good to yourself" with food during this transition period, be good to yourself by trimming down and changing your shape in anticipation of the exciting things to come.

Consider your makeup and how it can be changed. It's a good investment to see a makeup consultant at a department store or makeup salon. The fee is usually about $15 to design a new makeup. You don't have to buy all eighty-nine jars of makeup and creams the consultant may recommend. Just watch carefully, see what he does, and crib the best ideas for The New You.

Otherwise, experiment by yourself. Are your eyebrows too

thick, too thin, too crooked? Do they give you a downcast expression you could change with just a few strokes of pencil? Eyelids, lashes, face shapers, mouth coloring and contour can each separately and all together cause amazing changes in your appearance.

Be ruthless with your figure if it's gone to pot.

Don't be ashamed to spend time and money on yourself. The investment is for the rest of your life. A fur coat might just as well be a slipcover if your stuffing is fat and squashy underneath.

For a woman who feels "dumped" at forty or fifty, I feel anything and everything goes.

If you've hated your nose for years, or have bags under your eyes, or a double chin, why not see a plastic surgeon? If you're twenty pounds overweight and your skin is a mess, invest in a few weeks at a health farm. Why spend money for a vacation in the sun if you look lousy and won't enjoy it!

Perspective and proportion are essential to survival.

Travel, volunteer work, or a new career in the business world are all good ideas but only if you feel that you look your best. It's no boost to your morale to slink around Europe unless you're going to get more out of it than a cup of tea in a drafty castle.

> Make new friends, keep the old.
> One is silver, the other is gold.

Old friends are a mixed blessing. They hate it when you change the image they have cherished. As for being gold, Golden Age Club is more like it. It's tough advice to give, tougher to follow, but you must be friends with old friends on your terms and not theirs. If they disapprove of your new, younger appearance, that's their problem, not yours. Obviously, you don't want to look like a Medicare Twiggy in knee socks sucking a lollipop, but if you have a young figure, you can wear "In" clothes till you're ninety (and then hand them down to your seventy-five-year-old friends!)

New friends are a new world. Meet them by learning a new language, taking a course, getting involved in politics and local charities.

An inspiring example of this is the story of Lucille de George. A warmhearted, active woman, she found herself alone in her middle years. Of Italian descent, she had enormous pride in her heritage but was bothered by the stereotype of Italian women doing little more than running to church in shawls, having babies and cooking pizza and spaghetti. She decided to devote her new freedom to changing that image.

That was in 1956, she recalled later. "I didn't want to spend the rest of my life shopping for hats so I started American-Italian Awards (AMITA)—an organization to honor the contributions of Italian-American women."

In the ensuing years, AMITA has developed into a most worthwhile foundation, as rewarding for Lucille de George as for those helped through its scholarship program. Each year AMITA pays tribute to twelve outstanding women of Italian-American background at a fabulous ball. Proceeds of the ball and the AMITA journal go to the AMITA Scholarship Fund which provides for the artistic training of talented children. While the twelve women honored each year must be Italian, the children who benefit from the scholarship fund are not necessarily. They are chosen solely for their potential in music, acting, dancing and painting.

Among the AMITA award winners have been women in the arts as well as business, government, and the professions. They include Lucia Albanese, Fedora Bontempi, Anne Bancroft, Jessica Dragonette, Connie Francis, Mrs. John Cabot Lodge, and the Mayor of Hartford, Connecticut, Antonina P. Uccello. I, too, was a recipient—for Business in 1962.

The most difficult part of being suddenly alone is learning to function as "I" instead of "We" and learning that a lone woman can attend parties and meetings by herself without stigma. In fact, your new role can be extremely challenging.

As a Loner, learn how to say, "No." I'm not talking about sex. I'm talking about the notion people get that because you haven't a husband, "you've got nothing to do." You've got plenty to do. Yes, of course, you will baby-sit for friends in an emergency, but, no, you're not the Old Auntie who should be grateful to be invited for dinner even though it turns out Bob and Sue have to go to the PTA afterwards and would you mind staying with the kids till they get back?

Old Auntie—*no!* Auntie Mame—*si!*

Last but not least is a bedtime story for the Suddenly Alone. There is one advantage of having nobody around to see you in bed (for the time being, anyhow). That is, you can indulge in some home beauty treatments that are a bit off-putting for double-bed occupancy.

Slather yourself in nourishing creams without fear of being greasy. You will be greasy, but who cares? This is a good idea the night before you send the sheets to the laundry.

Give your hair an overnight scalp treatment, your face a night-mask that would scare a burglar. Cream your hands lavishly and slip on some washable cotton gloves. If you wake up in the middle of the night, watch out for mirrors. You're liable to startle even yourself.

In these days of exciting technology and incredible wonders in cosmetics and health, most barriers to beauty are down. Don't worry about breaking rules. Make your own rules.

Be prepared to meet and greet your second and yes, your third time around. Why not? You only live once so make the most of each and every opportunity. It's no disgrace to have a few wrinkles and to be able to look back over a few years. There may be snow on the roof but you can color it any shade you choose. The fact that it's there doesn't mean the fire in the furnace is burning any less fiercely.

Cruel but often true, the best thing that could happen to many a wife between the ages of forty and sixty is to be left without a husband. To say the least, it makes her sit up and take notice. To say the most, it makes her see herself not as the bride she was but as the woman she has become.

The challenge is frightening, but it is also exciting. Your future life is on the line, my fair lady, so be your own Henry Higgins and make yourself over. Are the few signs of age, the few extra pounds, and the few gray hairs going to defeat you?

"Nobody wants you when you're old and gray," the song goes. Make up your mind: "There'll be some changes made!" Today.

The Young Grandmother

It's unfair to mention Marlene Dietrich. She's a phenomenon. A super-woman. Joan Crawford and Gloria Swanson belong in the Super-trooper category, too. All three are incredibly

beautiful, disciplined women with a background of film training and experience and a determination to beat the camera at
its own game.

I salute such women for their triumph over time. They are
almost beyond the reach of most of us. More down to earth
are such beautiful, vivacious, young grandmothers as Betty
Furness, Mary Martin, Virginia Graham, Joan Bennett, Lady
Bird Johnson and Gypsy Rose Lee.

These are women to emulate. They look young and are full
of *bazzaz* without trying to be mini-boppers. They share
many characteristics worth examination by every woman who
is dandling her grandchildren and wondering if life is over for
her.

What these women have in common is an intense interest
in what is going on in the world. They have reached a stage of
personal development where each has a distinctive and personal approach to beauty and the self. However, this doesn't
mean that Betty Furness won't change her hairstyle or coloring. Or that Lady Bird doesn't go on a diet or have her skirts
shortened. Or that Joan Bennett won't find a new career in
television after years in films.

Hermione Gingold, the fabulous English actress and come-
dienne, is a warm and hilariously witty woman. People of all
ages adore her and compete for her companionship. The
mother of grown sons, Hermione tosses off the age question
by saying, "My sons are older than I am."

I remember meeting Gloria Swanson at an informal party
at the Harris Masterson's Dakota apartment in New York City
during one of their short jaunts away from Texas. Gloria
Swanson looked unbelievably young and I understand her

secret is a ruthlessly strict diet of special foods. Giving her real competition was our hostess, a gorgeous and youthful woman whose joy in being a grandmother is evident from the pictures of her grandchildren displayed throughout the apartment.

These days, Grandmas and Grandpas are kicking up their heels and having fun everywhere you look. At Trude Heller's place in Palm Beach, Warren and I met a couple from Passaic, New Jersey. They'd been married forty years and were dancing up a storm. She looked great and he still obviously appreciated her. It was wonderful. I hope Warren and I can get around the dance floor that fast when we've been married that long.

Another time, in Bermuda, we met a vivacious, attractive couple, the Howard Wolffs, Americans who live in Ocho Rios, Jamaica. They appeared to be in their fifties and were glowing with happiness. It turned out that the trip to Bermuda was their honeymoon, and as we got acquainted over drinks, what did they show us? Pictures of their respective grandchildren. Old enough to have grandchildren, proud of their past lives, they were building a new future together with joy and enthusiasm.

Mary Edson, Houston socialite, is a perfect example—a modern-day grandmother who became a producing artist, with a permanent gallery in one of Houston's finest art shops.

Once you're a grandmother, much of your appearance is a reflection of how you feel inside. Charm, animation, enthusiasm, and an insatiable interest in people are additional assets in your beauty bank by the time some dewy toddler puts you in your place with a chirping cry, "Grandma!"

Grandma's Bank Account

It's never too late to save your beauty. These are the things that add up to a sizable fund of loveliness before you know it. Regularly deposit:

An extra hour of sleep.
A brisk walk in good shoes.
A relaxed lunch with a good friend.
A new interest (or renewed activity on an old interest).
Regular health check-ups.
Participation in family and community affairs.

The Young Grandmother has the world on a string. Your chickens have flown the coop. The old henhouse is looking pretty neat without all those little feet tracking it up. You're queen of the roost now. Preen your feathers. Have as good a time as Betty, Mary, Virginia, Joan, Lady Bird, and Gypsy.

The Swinging Sixties

I'm proud to say I have a few older sisters who are swinging and *over* sixty—and darling, if you can swing at sixty, you don't need any advice from me! In fact, here's my phone number (212) LT 1-2900. Call me collect and let me know how you do it. This offer is good only to Swinging Sixties. If you just want to chew my ear off with complaints, don't call me, I'll call you!

You're As Old As You Feel

You've seen old ladies of twenty-five who have given up. You've seen high-flying great grandma's of eighty who can't get enough of that wonderful stuff known as being alive. You and your passport know how old you actually are but how old do you feel? What stage of life are you in?

To find out, take the following test. Be honest with yourself. (Big Sister is watching *you*.)

1. In the past five years, you have changed your hairstyle
   a) frequently.   b) occasionally.   c) not at all.
2. In planning a vacation, you prefer
   a) taking a chance on a brand new place.
   b) going back to the same, reliable place.
   c) staying home.
3. When you meet new people, your first reaction is:
   a) "Great—the more the merrier."
   b) "Let's find out more about them—maybe they won't fit in."
   c) "Who needs them? We have enough friends as it is."
4. If you were given $1,000 and had to spend it immediately, you would
   a) take a trip to Europe.
   b) use it for a child's education.
   c) refurnish the living room.
5. Given a limit of buying only one new thing to wear for the winter, you would choose
   a) the newest, most way-out outfit on the market.
   b) a mink jacket.
   c) a couturier suit.

ANSWERS: 3–5 *a*. You are the Eternal Teen, eager and hungry for new experience, ready to try anything, wonderfully alive and open to the wonders of the world.

   3–5 *b*. You are the Earth Mother, protecting your nest and your values from outside intrusion, cautious

43

about change, hesitant to risk hard-won advantages against questionable delights.

   3–5 c. You are the Dowager Duchess. There's fight in the old girl yet but it's hemmed in by stiff, unyielding corsets of bygone times.

The Three Phases
of Eve

God has given you one face,
and you make yourselves another.

Shakespeare, Hamlet, *Act III*

Have you ever realized that you never actually see your own face? Think about it for a minute. You see a reflection of your face in a mirror. You see photographs and portraits. You may see your "face" in your children who look like you. Or the reaction of people who look at you. But all the days of your life, the one face you carry with you twenty-four hours a day is the one face you will never see in the living flesh.

I make this point for three reasons. For one, it fascinates me as an irony of life that the face we present to the world is the one we never truly see ourselves. Second, it shows how much a woman's appearance depends on a clear, flawless mirror and good lighting. Finally, it dramatizes the need for every woman to become a proficient portrait painter with a sound knowledge of the anatomy of her face and the artistic skills to create the most beautiful picture possible.

Making up your face is like doing a three-dimensional self-portrait in glowing color. You have to know about contour, about shading, about texture—and all in relation to the basic canvas that is your complexion.

As you can see from the three simple drawings which follow, the Face of Eve is divided into three phases: Eyes, Nose, Mouth. My hypothesis is that you must consider each phase separately to see what improvement can be made. Then, view all three in combination to judge how they balance and harmonize with each other.

For instance, if your eyes and nose are large and your mouth is almost nonexistent, your portrait-painting problem is both to improve the contour of your mouth and to bring your mouth into better proportion with the other features by making it larger.

Your Eyes

Shape, coloring, and makeup mean nothing if your eyes are dull and tired-looking. Sleep is essential for sparkling, exciting eyes and the skin area around them. Close your eyes for a

Fig. 1

few seconds whenever you can—in an elevator, talking on the phone, waiting for the kettle to boil. This relaxes the eyes and renews the restorative fluids.

Where air pollution is high, soothe and clean the eyes daily with a mild, commercial eye lotion, or plain warm water. Ugly and painful inflammations of the eyelid can be avoided with a little preventive care.

If your eyes are your best feature, they are probably large with strong color and an interesting shape. Before applying makeup, study the shape. Are they round? Almond-shaped? Do they turn up or droop down in the outer corners? Are they too close to your nose? too widely spaced? Do your brows and lashes have definition or are they pale?

To my mind, eye-liner can be your best friend or your worst enemy. It can enhance your eye shape, or make you look like a clown in a fourth-rate circus. The idea is to use eye-liner to achieve exactly what you want and nothing more. A friend of mine, after weeks of experimenting, uses liner only in the center of her lids to make her eyes appear round. While round eyes are not the usual ambition, she discovered that "rounding" her eyes made her long, thin face seem fuller.

Another girl has eyes that droop slightly. When she extends the eye-liner, she looks like a very sad, basset hound. In contrast, a thickish coat of eye-liner that ends just before the corner of her eye, gives her an alert, lively look.

The color of your eyes can be highlighted in several ways. Of course, you can change the color entirely with tinted contact lenses. If you like your own color and merely want it to come on stronger, use a darker shade of shadow that either matches your eyes or contrasts sharply with them.

With pale blue eyes, a bright cerulean blue is a good color. With gray eyes, turquoise is exciting. Brown and hazel eyes usually have flecks of green or blue and even yellow. Use these for heightening just as you might pick out a thread in a dress or suit fabric for accenting with gloves or a scarf.

A good overall plan for eye makeup is the Three Layer technique that models use. With your own personal variations, you will find it flattering to all eyes.

THREE-LAYER LOOK

Apply white or ivory shadow on your upper lid, directly under your eyebrows, for brightness. Smooth a one-eighth-inch-wide line of brown along the eyelid crease to deepen your eyes. Apply a glowing shade of shadow on the lower lid to match your eyes or your outfit.

Outline your upper lashes with eye-liner as discussed.

MASCARA

I believe in lots of mascara. It makes me "feel" my eyes. Being aware of them, I use them more actively to "see" the job at hand and really connect visually with whomever I am working. My own private technique consists of using two separate roll-on mascara brushes. One with the extra little flecks; one plain. I won't leave the house without four (count 'em, FOUR) coats of mascara. The problem is that each coat must dry thoroughly and your lady Eve is always in a hurry! What I do is apply the first layer with the flecks and then rush around putting on my girdle and stockings while my lashes dry. For the second layer I use the plain wand to fill in the spaces around the flecks. Then, into my shoes and dress while that dries. Next layer, more flecks, while I make a phone call or two or write a note for the maid. Finally, the last layer of plain roll-on to extend the lashes as I like them, brush my hair, put on some lipstick, slam on my hat—and out the door to work.

To let you in on a tiny secret, I still use an old-fashioned eyelash curler. It makes me feel very glamorous for some reason. I like the effect of false eyelashes but I can never get them on. My best advice here is to try them. A friend of mine wears them every day of her life and gets them on in seconds. She thinks mascara is barbaric: "Who needs all that mud on your eyelids?"

She admits spending a few months and ruining a few pairs of false lashes before she mastered the technique but now she doesn't know how she lived without them.

If you've never worn false lashes, get your first lesson from a friend or at the beauty bar of a department store or drugstore. Have your first pair professionally shaped for your eyelids so you don't look like Minnie Mouse.

EYEBROWS

They determine the expression of your eyes. If they are too heavy, you seem to be glowering. If they are too light, your eyes lack a definite frame. If they zoom upward and outward too wildly, you may look like a startled dragon-lady. If they curve down around your eyes, it may give you an air of permanent mourning.

The arch of your brow may be a problem. A simple approach is to take a pencil and hold it upright alongside the outer corner of your eye. At whatever point the pencil hits your eyebrow, that's the best place for the arch—with the rest of the brow tapering gently outward and downward from there.

EXPRESSION

You can wear a $50-brand eye makeup with diamond dust sent by DeBeers himself, but if your eye expression is cold, calculating or disinterested, you might just as well wear eye-patches. Eyes are the windows of your personality. They also reflect your interest, enthusiasm and warmth.

We are admonished from childhood to "Use your head!" I say, "Use your eyes, too!" Let them do some of your talking for you. Once you start to think with your eyes, you will see how much more completely you can express yourself and how much more quickly and easily you reach people.

Note to Squinters: Squinting gives a woman's face a nosy-old-lady look. It causes premature wrinkles around the eyes. If you do squint, it may be merely a bad habit that you can break—or you may need glasses. These days, glasses are so becoming, some women wear frames with plain glass just to have the fashion effect. If specs offend you completely, contact lenses can take away that unattractive "squint."

Your Nose

If you can honestly look at your nose in the mirror and say, "This is the most beautiful nose in the world," all I can say is, "Who's your plastic surgeon?"

Fig. 2

The nose is the only part of your face that you can do very little about, apart from a surgical adjustment known to the gang as a "Nose Job." If your nose is too big, you're in trouble. It is a solid, three-dimensional contour. I hate to see women kidding themselves with dark shadings on the sides and light makeup on the tip of the nose and along the bone. This is fine for photography. If you're having your picture taken, by all means create some sculpture illusion with dark pancake makeup or shadow to make your nose appear slimmer. But don't go out in the street or to a party with a pound of mud on your nose. You'll look as if you walked into a door.

I think it's important for every woman with a large nose to

face the fact that there is nothing dramatic that can be done. If your nose distresses you, surgery is incredibly successful and costs about the same as a fun fur. The results can be astounding in terms of your physical as well as psychological beauty.

Whatever the shape of your nose, may I stress the old Jimmy Cagney expression, "Keep your nose clean!" What I mean is keep the outside of your nose and the pores around it well scrubbed. Blackheads, enlarged pores, and surface blemishes are anything but pretty. Also, if summer sun or winter wind tend to light up your nose like Rudolph's, use a sunscreen base on your nose and apply a light shade of makeup on it when you start out. The color will adjust itself.

About the only creative crumb of help I can offer has to do with your overall facial portrait. If you have a large nose with smallish eyes and mouth, you can make your nose seem a bit smaller by making your eyes and mouth bigger.

Your Mouth

It's more than your two lips. It's your teeth, your smile, your pout. It's a combination of shape, texture, and color. Your mouth both talks for you and about you.

Most men respond to a full, lush mouth with a glowing kissable color. The exact shape of the lips and color lipstick used are things which change with style. In the past forty years, lip shapes have gone from bee-stung blobs of the twenties to the heavy purple slash of the forties to the no-mouth of the sixties. The clever girl uses the current fad as a point of departure and adapts it to her own particular need.

Fig. 3

LIPS

To me, texture, teeth and mouth expression are as important as shape. The contour of the mouth can be changed at will with the aid of a lipbrush and outliner. You can experiment to discover the best shape for your face, wiping away each trial as you go. Texture is something many women neglect. Dry, furrowed, scaly lips are a horror. If they are really bad, see a doctor—you may have a deficiency of some kind. Otherwise, use moisture cream under your lipstick or use a moisturized foundation base and choose a creamy lipstick, as well.

In applying a night cream, don't skip your lips. Give them an extra dollop of lubricant. Helpful, too, is to pat on a generous layer of baby oil or cold cream before getting into a hot tub. The steam will help the cream to soften and smooth your lips. (And don't forget the corners!)

TEETH

You can have the world's most devastating mouth but if you have stained teeth, don't bother to smile. You'll wreck everything! Teeth cleanliness is as important to health as to beauty. Some women spend a fortune on their hair but won't go to the dentist twice a year for a professional cleaning. Smokers have the worst of it. Nobody sings, "I dream of Jeannie with the light brown teeth!"

In the last ten years, dentistry techniques have improved fantastically. I'm not going to play Dentist with you, but I would like to suggest, in particular to you women over thirty, that you don't have to spend the rest of your beautiful lives with a Terry Thomas space or crooked front teeth. Many of today's women who were children during the depression and World War II needed braces and correction but couldn't have them because of hard times and the shortage of dentists in wartime. Later, they thought, "Well, it's too late for that!"

It's not too late. Orthodontia is no longer the sole preserve of little kids. A friend of mine in her thirties recently wore a wire retainer on her front teeth for six months. It closed up the space that has haunted her since her teens. She was elated. "Maybe nobody notices the difference, but I do! I smile all the time." Looking at some old snapshots, she realized she never smiled for the camera and that her mouth always looked scrunched up to hide her teeth.

If you are self-conscious about your teeth, you will hold your mouth unattractively. Perhaps you will acquire mouth mannerisms such as pursing your lips or covering your teeth with your upper lip or smiling in a crooked, inhibited way. It makes you and others feel good if you can smile wholeheartedly, no holds barred—and no holes bared!

EXPRESSION

As for expression, all you have to do is walk along the street and watch mouths. The tight, taut, down-turned mouth makes the person wearing it ugly no matter what the rest of the face or figure is like. My mother used to warn me not to make a funny face as a child. "It will freeze like that!"

The woman who habitually wears a disgruntled, sour expression is going to find it "frozen" on her face. After the age of thirty, the face becomes a reflection of personality as well as beauty. Laughing eyes and a smiling mouth become part of the permanent expression. As lines inevitably begin to appear, laugh lines are certainly more becoming than frown furrows and pout marks.

As an experiment, look in the mirror. Smile. See how the mouth becomes soft and the eyes light up? Okay. Growl. Make believe you're confronting your worst enemy. See how menacing you look? It's fine to look ugly in order to scare your opponents, but even then, you can generally win more with a smile.

Beauty Buds from the Garden of Eve

1. Experiment with beauty brushes and applicators until you find the kind you can handle easily. Keep them religiously CLEAN.

2. Think of yourself as Rembrandt when you start to do your self-portrait. Make sure that the canvas (your skin) is clean and primed and that the lighting is good.

3. In summer, keep colognes, lotions, and astringents, in the refrigerator for extra zing. If you buy lipsticks in quantity, keep those not in use in the refrigerator, too.

4. Powder blushers are marvelous. Or, use a little lipstick on your fingertips for an exact match. For a dewy, moist finish, add a passing touch of night cream to the blush area. A sheen is more youthful looking than a flat, powdery finish.

5. Cold water is one of the best beauty aids. Splash it on your face. Take an ice-cold shower. When tired, plunge your arms into cold water at least to above the wrists (above the elbow is even better). The coldness stimulates blood circulation and makes the skin tingly and firm.

6. Don't worry unduly about perspiration. People who perspire a lot generally have good skin.

7. If you have a weekend cottage or take lots of trips, keep a makeup case packed with duplicates of all your beauty and grooming needs. This way, you can rest assured of always having essentials. You won't be worried about forgetting your night cream or bath oil and you won't delude yourself that you can pack in four minutes.

8. To the women who ask, "Do beauty creams really do any good?" let me quote Ruth Flaster who owns and operates the cosmetic factory that produces "Eve Nelson" and other famous products: "They can't hurt!" My theory is, I don't care what you use on your face and body as long as you use something that will lubricate it. Use lard, use mayonnaise— just so that it moisturizes, softens, nourishes and keeps skin soft and supple.

9. Take care of your feet. Keep them soothed, smoothed, and

pedicured. Lines in the face often start with tired, aching feet.

10. Don't be a pushover for Magic. Beware of products which promise too much. A man may make you feel twenty years younger but no product in this world is going to make you look twenty years younger. When something dramatic appears on the scene, analyze it carefully. A few years ago, a new "face-lift" lotion hit the market. It did "lift" the skin and tighten the face . . . for a few hours. It *also* stretched the elasticity of the skin, causing it to sag more than before the lotion was applied. Any woman who used this product over a period of time would find her skin losing whatever elasticity it had.

Use your head about what you use on your face.

Just Call Me the Duchess of Bath

I spend a lot of beauty time in the bathtub, thinking, resting, and getting gorgeous all over. To me, a bath is a beauty cocktail. It relaxes and restores the body and is an enjoyable transition between work and play.

To put it mildly, I'm a complete nut about bath oil. In fact, it's a good thing I manufacture it because the Nelsons would have the biggest bath-oil bill in the country. At home, Warren and I have separate bathrooms. On trips, however, we've worked out a system for him to take his shower first because, otherwise, the tub would be too slippery after my beauty bath.

Since I designed my Eve Nelson "Creation" Bath Oil, I am partial to it. My thinking was to have refreshing, soothing oil with almost no scent so that you can add a drop or two of whatever perfume you're in the mood for.

As with body and face emollients, use whatever bath preparations that please you—so long as you use something! Water and soap are much too drying by themselves.

Through the Bathroom Door: Answers to some frequently asked questions:

1. I love bath oil, but I take showers. What can I use?
   Answer: Spray oil cologne, made by several companies.
2. My skin is very delicate. How can I care for it?
   Answer: A milk bath is soothing.
3. I feel beat after a hot bath. How can I pep myself up?
   Answer: Give yourself an alcohol or friction rubdown.
4. What can I do for dry skin?
   Answer: After your bath, apply moisture lotion all over.
5. I'm always in a hurry. How can I get my clothes to slip on easily on my still-damp body?
   Answer: That's where dusting powder comes in. It absorbs dampness and smooths the skin.

A short time ago, I was interviewed by a newspaper writer who asked me a question that set me thinking. She said, "You are an authority on beauty. You have your choice of all the beauty products made. You know your personal beauty needs and problems. Now—suppose you were stranded on a desert isle and could have your choice of five beauty aids and no more, what would they be?"

I really had to think about that. In effect, I would have to select five items for beauty survival until some big yacht with a handsome captain arrived to save me. Finally, I narrowed my choices down to these: 1) Mascara; 2) Lipstick; 3) Moisturized sun lotion which is good protection against the elements as well as a softener for the face and body; 4) Hair-brush and 5) Cleansing Lotion or Cream.

What would be your desert-island beauty plan?

On my travels to our various stores and Eve Nelson salons and in my work for social organizations, I meet women who tell me their husbands complain about the time and money they spend on "being beautiful." I have a feeling that most of these husbands are teasing their wives. Men want their women to be attractive and exciting. Because of mass production, beauty preparations are available to fit every budget. There is no excuse but laziness for not putting your best face forward.

The next time that other face in the bathroom mirror (the face with the shaving cream on it) makes a crack about all your bottles and jars, here are a few things to tell him to make him glad he's living in the twentieth century.

Tell him the girls of ancient Babylonia stained the soles of their feet red with henna and touched up their breasts with purple dye. Tell him women in the court of Queen Elizabeth I used white lead to whiten their complexions and glazed their faces with egg white. Tell him nineteenth-century Chinese noblewomen let their fingernails grow six inches and painted them gold as a sign of rank.

Tell him, too, that the main reason you spend time, effort, and money is to be beautiful for yourself and for the beautiful people in your life, mainly him.

Tell him that a woman who suffers from The Uglies can't act Pretty.

Then, tell him to indulge himself in some of the new male grooming aids and join in the fun of looking and feeling his best.

How to Take a Man Away from His Wife

You've been watching him lately. Suddenly, you know! He's ripe for a change. He's got all the earmarks of falling out of love with his wife. He may not know it yet himself but all the signs are there.

He's restless, not quite with it or the group. Tuned out. Detached. He doesn't seem to have much to say to his wife except the mundane things—the heavy traffic, the heavy bills, the unpredictable children, and the changeable weather. He's not rude to her but he forgets things. It's almost as if she weren't around, as if she were a shadow figure gradually disappearing from view. In fact, he looks but he just doesn't *see* her anymore.

The man who is falling out of love with his wife is going to be grabbed up by someone and soon. It might as well be you.

Now, just how do you take a man away from his wife?

Start by taking a long, penetrating look at the wife. What went wrong? How did the bride he loved become the neglected woman he merely tolerates? Analyze *her* and profit from *her* mistakes. The trouble didn't start yesterday at breakfast.

Okay, you've guessed it. It's *your husband* we're talking about and *you are the wife* we're talking to!

This taking a penetrating look isn't done with mirrors. It's done objectively and requires introspection. When I ask you to look at the "she"—the wife we're talking to is you.

Ready? Set? Let's play the game.

Does "she" act as if she's entitled?

She's smug about the ring on her third finger left hand. She acts as if she feels "entitled" to all the material rewards of a hard-working husband. She has forgotten the girls who earn their own way and who can make The Man feel like a king for the smallest generosity which *she* takes for granted.

She takes what he has to give without appreciation and then asks for more. It never occurs to her that he might be thinking of spending his money elsewhere. She is scrupulous about teaching their children to say, "Thank you," but has forgotten how to say it herself, to her husband, with a smile, really meaning it, and wanting him to know she understands how hard he works.

There are a few more things this "entitled" lady does. She *measures* what her sisters, neighbors, and bridge club friends have, particularly the size of their dining rooms and how many fur coats in their closets. Somehow, she only relates to those with more than she has. She continues to project these comparisons at every opportunity in the belief that this will inspire her husband to greater success and that she is a great lady.

Nothing kills the golden-egg-laying goose quicker than a grabby goose girl. The wife with a case of the "gimme's" will eventually (if not now) find herself on the wrong end of the trade deal. A wife who uses sexual blackmail to get what she wants may find it works—for a while. There's too much free-wheeling affection available for him to have to pay for what is rightfully his at home.

Rather than you feeling entitled to everything, let him feel pleasure in being the one man entitled to give you your heart's desire. You can make his gifts as much a pleasure for him to give as for you to receive. Part of giving is the pleasure in seeing the reactions of the recipient.

Your thank you will both please him and encourage him to dream up new little "goodies" to delight and excite you.

Apart from material things, there are the gifts of thoughtfulness and consideration that a woman should appreciate and for which she should make known her appreciation. It's basic human psychology to like being thanked. The basic things two people can give each other are thoughtfulness and caring.

Show The Man that you care about him and that you appreciate his thoughtfulness to you, and you've got something brewing.

An important point to make about gifts is the gift of your time and energy. How often does this very desirable husband say to his wife, "Come on, honey. We're going to the football game!" Does she jump into her stadium boots, sprinkle a little perfume behind her knees and fill up her hip flask for that cold, cold final quarter? No. Too often, self-pity bathes the room with a baleful gloom as she says, "I have too much to do."

What she means is, she doesn't like sports and being with her husband isn't enough to lure her out into the fresh air. Personally, I put sports in about the same category as painting portraits on velvet but when Warren says we're going to West Point this Saturday, I put on my most comfortable shoes because he likes to walk 90,000 miles. When he watches the out-of-town games on television on weekends, I am one wife that's happy. I like having him comfortable and content at home instead of who-knows-where watching who-knows-whose set? Anyway, it's his home, isn't it?

Just so you're not blinded by my gorgeous halo, I might add right here that when opera season rolls around, Warren is sweet as pie about taking me despite his affliction with the original Tin Ear. After all, who said I was entitled to a Beethoven for a husband?

Has "she" forgotten how to flirt with him?

She has stashed away the old wedding pictures and with them the feminine wiles that lured him to the altar in the first place. She doesn't bother to tease him anymore, forgetting that good-natured teasing ends in laughter and laughter is momentary happiness. When the laughter is gone, the happiness remains.

Has she stopped acting like he really turns her on? Does she feel it's too much bother to cook up his favorite dish? or to dream up a sentimental gift to celebrate a sentimental occasion?

Has she stopped playing up to his ego? Can't she see that compliments build him up, especially in front of other people and particularly in front of the children?

She no longer treats him like a lover. She has allowed the electric wires between them to go slack and the juice just can't get through—and if it does, the light it gives off is pretty dim.

Excitement and surprise are delightful stimulations for a

man. You've heard the happy husband say, "That woman! I love her because I never know what she's going to do next! Who can figure her out?"

The successful husband-grabber is the woman who knows that ability to attract and delight men should be a continuing part of her life and not one that ends the minute she gets married or hooks her man. The successful wife is the one who enjoys being with men, talking with men, sparring with men on various subjects—and who refuses to allow her parties to deteriorate into segregated groups of women in one corner, men in the other.

Flirting with a man means keeping him aware of his manliness and your femininity and making him glad about both. Gentle teasing (as opposed to malicious teasing) is a good technique. In other words, do tease him about his broad, beautiful shoulders, but lay off the receding hairline. Build him up; don't knock him down.

Show him spontaneous signs of affection. Unnerve him (ever so slightly) at a party by whispering something erotic in his ear or through secret codes that come out spontaneously in a group situation.

Buy him an unexpected present when there's no reason— "just because" you thought of him, or because this sweater would look great on the golf course, or because you remembered he wanted some new driving gloves.

Fuss over him. Straighten his tie. Brush off his jacket. Puff up the pillows if he's lying on the couch. Take off his shoes when he's stretched out reading. He may say, "Leave me alone," or "You really shouldn't bother," but lady, bother!

Write him a poem. Draw him a crazy picture. Cut out an

appropriate cartoon. Slip these into his coat pocket, his brief-case, inside his tennis racket case or golf bag, tape them to the wheel of the car—the delicious surprise will make him both feel great and think about how great you make him feel!

Once, on a Caribbean cruise, I watched a wife flirt with her husband. She was obviously crazy about him and wanted him to be happy. Her instincts served her well. To the group at our table, she never missed the opportunity to say, in front of her husband, "Isn't he wonderful? . . . I know I shouldn't talk this way about my own husband, but he's absolutely great!"

Later, in the lounge, she would tease him about being the best dancer, and would tell him that other girls were dying to dance with him. I've never seen a young husband have such a good time, basking in the warmth of his wife's appreciation.

In a way, it reminded me of another vacation trip Warren and I made, to Aruba. We had both been working very hard and we were so happy to be away from people, we steered clear of the other guests during the first few days. We asked for a table for two in the dining room with iced champagne awaiting us every night. Our two lounge chairs were apart from the others near the pool. We drank in the sunshine, rubbed tanning lotion on each other, and laughed a lot. When other guests tried to start a conversation, we answered with noncommittal grunts that said, "Go 'way. Don't bother us."

When we finally got the kinks out and began to feel socia-ble, we discovered the other guests had been speculating about us. They were surprised to find out we were actually married!

"The way you two were clowning around and wanting to

be alone—we thought you must be his mistress!" one of the women confided to me.

I've thought about what she said many times. Her words made me realize that being a wife means being a mistress as well.

Does "she" look older than he does?

Her figure is still quite good, despite the children, but she slumps over. Her tummy isn't big but she lets it sag. Her chin and jawline wouldn't look thick and droopy if she held her head up. Her mouth is turned down in the corners in dissatisfaction and nothing adds years to a woman's face more than a sourpuss expression. Her hair is limp and the gray hairs are worn as a mournful badge of honor. She likes to think, "I earned every one of them." Who cares? Give her a medal.

Solving this problem is like taking candy from a baby— only don't eat the candy, it's got too many calories! In today's miracle world, there's no such thing as an "older woman"— not until she's ready for a Senior Village, anyway! By this, I don't mean a grown woman should walk around looking like a teeny-bopper. What I do mean is every woman can have an acceptable figure, hair that invites a man to run his fingers through it, skin he feels compelled to touch and, most important, a fundamentally feminine personality that makes him feel fundamentally a man.

Looking older than you should is a crime against nature. It's as if a beautiful flower were neglected and allowed to wither and die before its time, or a lovely antique table were left out in the yard to crack and warp when a little polish and care would sustain, and maybe even increase, its beauty.

The three most important areas to concentrate on are:
FIGURE. HAIR. FACIAL EXPRESSION.

Figure: Straighten up and feel right. If you allow yourself to slump over, you will feel slumpy and look like some care-worn field worker with as much sex appeal as a crumpled newspaper. Why do you think soldiers are commanded to stand up straight? Not only because it looks better but because it makes each soldier feel stronger, livelier, and prouder. Standing up straight allows you to breathe more deeply, too. Never forget that the influx of oxygen revives your body and invigorates your entire being.

Clear out your wardrobe. Get rid of ugly, defeating items. Think about his wife. Does she wear old slacks that make her look like a buffalo's mother? Do her bra straps hang out, including the rusty safety pin? Is she still "getting wear" out of a cocktail dress that hits her in all the wrong places?

Try on everything, from foundation garments to formal wear. The foundation garments are most important, for two reasons. If they don't fit or are worn out, they make your figure look lumpy and dowdy. Stretched-out garters, sagging panels, and lumpy zippers make you feel uncomfortable—and when you feel uncomfortable, you look uncomfortable.

It's better to have a small wardrobe of clothes that "do something" for your figure than a large collection, half-filled with hideous mistakes. If you've made a mistake and bought a dress that looks as if your worst enemy chose it for you, get rid of it. So you spent money on it—but why compound the error by suffering even more. By getting rid of the "gruesomes," you are never tempted to wear one, even around the house.

This husband you're after—what part of the female anatomy does he most admire? If you don't know, listen and watch him at a party. His comments will tell you a lot. Concentrate on the parts of your anatomy that coincide with his special areas of interest. For instance, if he admires shoulders and you've got great shoulders, make sure you wear something strapless, with a halter neck, or with shoe-string shoulder straps. Cream your shoulders and use a long-handled complexion brush when bathing to get rid of blemishes and scaly bits.

If he likes legs, choose your stockings and shoes with an eye to improving your leg shape. If he likes low-cut necklines, forget current fashions to the extent of wearing low-cut necklines at appropriate times. Most husbands don't know and don't care about the exact nuances of what's "In." The fashion models may be wearing silk shirts buttoned up to the throat. There's nothing to prevent you from unbuttoning the shirt halfway for the décolletage that entices this husband you want.

Hair: Maybe you've forgotten that hair is very exciting to a man. Not only that, but your own head of hair is vital to your personal pride in yourself as a woman. How you wear it should, again, reflect the taste of the husband who interests you. Pay attention to him. If he likes to tousle your hair or drive around in an open car with the wind beating at your hair, you'd better forget about a stiff coiffure which depends on lots of hair spray. He may joke about "all that glue" in your hair, but as someone once said, "Truth is often said in jest."

He might say to you, "Why don't you wear your hair the way you used to?" How did you wear it? Long? With bangs?

Back from the face? Very short and curly? The exact hairdo may be wrong for the changes in facial shape, but it's possible to adapt the style he likes and appeal to his nostalgia as well as his senses. It's like the soup Mother used to make.

Hair-coloring is essential. A woman with gray hair is only kidding herself when she smugly says, "My husband loves my gray hair." Perhaps one woman in a million looks fabulous with gray or white hair—and she is probably a striking beauty with strong features, dazzling blue eyes and bright white hair. Unless you look like that, color your hair!

And don't keep talking about it to the man you're trying to win—nor should you ask him how it looks, or remark about how much of a nuisance it is to maintain.

Most men are "color blind" to hair-coloring—unless, of course, you go from murky brown to sunbeam blonde in one afternoon. Even then, he will be intrigued by the change and there's nothing like intrigue to start a whole new dialogue between two people.

NOTE: If you change your hair color and styling drastically and he doesn't seem to notice right away, don't feel as if you've been hit by a truck. A man whose senses have been dulled by marriage may sometimes take a little time to get revved up again. He'll know "something" is different and that is certain to stir him up, if slowly.

A friend of mine, on a husband-grab mission, noticed that he kept pulling her hair back from her face, saying, "I want to see your face. The hair is in the way." She experimented with her hair and hit on a brushed-back style with the hair caught in a velvet bow at the nape of her neck. It worked wonders.

Healthy hair is lively, exciting hair—an extension of your own lively, exciting body. If your hair is in trouble, treat it as you would any other part of your body that isn't feeling well. Nourish it with rich shampoo and comforting creams. Exercise it with stimulating scalp massage and regular brushing.

If it's sickly, falling out, breaking off, limp and lank, take it to a doctor. A good dermatologist will tell you how to bring it back to health.

Facial Expression: With the tensions and pressures of contemporary life, husbands are confronted by faces that range from blank unfriendliness to outright hostility all day. To make a husband look forward to seeing your face, be actively aware of your facial expressions. By this, I don't mean you should be a grinning idiot twenty-four hours a day. What I do suggest is a determination to see the lighter side of dark situations, to radiate warmth and generosity in your face, to say in your expression, "What can I do for you?" instead of a petulant, "What have you done for me!"

A young wife I know is always being complimented by her husband for "her beautiful smile." He mentions it often and obviously basks in its warmth. I've looked at this girl's smile. Her teeth are slightly crooked and would never be picked for a toothpaste ad. They're white enough but not so that they would give you snow-blindness. The attraction is that she smiles easily and with her whole face, not the mouth alone. She is an enjoyer and includes you in her pleasure in being alive.

In terms of facial expression, I would say the mouth is the most important with the eyes a close second. A mouth that smiles easily, that refuses to be petulant, that is relaxed and not pinched tight in disapproval, will always look kissable and delicious.

Eyes can smile and caress as well. A man feels ten feet tall when he is suddenly aware of your eyes looking at him with warm approval across a room, crowded or otherwise.

When he's talking, your eyes should be alert and with him every step of the way, even if he doesn't let you get a word in edgewise. If you want this man, don't let your attention wander. It will show in your eyes and will give him a sense of rejection he will never mention and you will never know.

Some of the world's most exciting women from Sarah Bernhardt to Elizabeth Taylor have been praised for their eyes. The shape and color have rarely been mentioned. Rather, the tributes are always to the fire, excitement, wit and laughter emanating from them.

Does "she" make him feel unnecessary?

How? The children, her family, the community at large, all come first, ahead of him. He may like pot roast but the kids like lamb chops so he gets lamb chops. He may come home dog-tired wanting only a hug and a martini and what does he get handed to him as he walks through the door? You guessed it: the day's trials and tribulations in not a few well-chosen words. He may want sympathy after his harrowing day but gets drowned out by a blow-by-blow description of the wife-next-door's sinus trouble.

In contrast to this wife, here's what you do: Make him feel needed, wanted and utterly vital to your health and happiness.

Most men are responsible, hard-working, serious creatures. Today's whole social structure is based on the idea, "Women and children first!" He works hard to support a home and children. He feels a strong sense of obligation to provide the material comforts, vacations, cultural advantages and schooling.

He doesn't want to avoid these responsibilities but he will resent the attitude that paying the bills is his only excuse for being around. The husband whose wife makes him feel this way is ripe for plucking.

It's both easy and enjoyable to make a husband feel necessary. Instead of ignoring his special tastes, glorify them. If he likes roast beef hash, learn to make roast beef hash, with an egg on top. If he likes chocolate cake, be sure there's always a chocolate cake in the refrigerator for a late snack or an illegitimate raid on the kitchen.

Of course, at the other extreme, a wife can drive her husband out the door and down to the diner if she spends *all* her energies on cooking with food and not enough cooking with gas, as the gang used to say down at my neighborhood diner.

In fact, a good thing to remember is the old saw about the ardent husband who comes panting home to his new bride. He sweeps her into his arms. "But, dear—dinner's ready!" she protests.

"If I wanted food, I'd hire a cook!"

Or, as humorist Mark Wachs points out, there are other ways to a man's heart besides his stomach. He tells the story of the girl who visits the zoo and finds the monkey cage empty.

"Where are the monkeys?" she asks the attendant.

"In the back, making love."

"Do you think they'd come out for some peanuts?"

"Would you?"

One of the most husband-killing things a wife can do is to be efficient at the wrong time. At a recent dinner party I watched the host make the salad dressing at the table with evident pleasure. To his wife's growing annoyance, he stirred in the seasoning, added vinegar, tasted it, ground in some pepper, tasted it again. Unable to control her impatience, his wife snapped, "Hurry up. It's going to taste like fuel oil anyway!"

The point here is, her husband enjoys concocting a salad dressing. The guests are friends who like him and don't really care what the dressing tastes like. What's the difference if he makes a production of this harmless event?

By ruining this simple little moment of pleasure, the wife is pointing the way out the door and into another woman's arms.

By "losing" the small battles, you win the large victory of a contented, happy man. Many wives operate on a point system of perverse behavior. If the husband says, "Let's take in a movie," she would rather play cards. If the husband would like a quiet Sunday at home, she invites twenty people and has him racing around to set up the ice and clear away the Sunday papers before he's read them. She wants the living room to be a museum and all he wants is a comfortable place to sit.

Husbands usually give in rather than have a fight but mental arithmetic adds up and one day the balance gets so uneven, it goes tilt.

To take this man away from his wife, here's all you have to do:

Ten Primary Rules of Husband-grabbing

1. Knowing him and understanding him, imagine yourself in his shoes. From this vantage point, give his wife a thorough going-over to see what she does to bore, irritate or otherwise turn this man off.

2. Look at him as a brand new man in your life. Analyze his likes and dislikes, then romanticize his likes.

3. Appeal to his various appetites, and not just in the kitchen!

4. Create a sexual excitement, not necessarily in a black negligee but by your fun approach to life, your eternal youth, in the way you think, your ability to see humor in things that might otherwise be a disaster. These are the things that end in a kiss—and start, who knows? (Even if you're in your little print housecoat.)

5. Be sentimental about him and don't be afraid to show it. He'll welcome the softness of you in contrast to the cold, calculating world outside your doorstep.

6. Use subtlety, tact, and every ounce of femininity to get what you want—not a bulldozer.

7. Always be available when he needs you. If you'd rather be with him than anyone else in the world, remember that every minute you're with him. Don't waste time on subjects that don't particularly stimulate him, interest him or

excite him. By all means be ready to fit in with his unavoidable last-minute change of plans.

    8. Listen. Whatever else is going on, listen to *him*. This is the best way to keep up with what's going on *inside* him.

    9. Don't be depressed if he doesn't react instantly.

    10. Set yourself a starting deadline and go to it!

The marriage we propose to break up is the lumbering, faded old loveboat that is slowly heading for the falls unless the wife starts paddling fast in the opposite direction.

This could be your marriage, so lock out the OLD YOU and take her place with a new, improved product that will make joint housekeeping as exciting and rewarding as it was the day you were married.

What the OLD YOU has forgotten, the NEW YOU has to learn anew and keep as an active part of your life.

OLD YOU asks: "Do you love me? Why don't you ever say you love me?"

NEW YOU says: "I love you." She doesn't demand to be "loved." She understands that giving love generally generates lovingness. Demanding love turns the love faucet cold if not off.

OLD YOU thinks: "I've got a husband. I don't have to bother." She regards her wedding ring as an invisible ring around his neck that's attached to an invisible string which she controls.

NEW YOU thinks: "Thank heavens I've got a husband. If I don't bother, somebody else will. If I don't bother, maybe he won't bother to come home one of these nights."

OLD YOU considers sentimentality "foolishness for kids.

We're married now. Life is real and earnest and where are we going to get the money to pay for Janie's braces?"

NEW YOU recognizes the value of expressing joy and pleasure in marriage. Warren and I are very extravagant with each other at birthday and other celebration times, but I know the most successful gift I ever planned for him was a recording of *My Fair Lady* tunes, re-named, "My Fair Warren," with all the lyrics re-vamped to refer to him. I had a picture of him enlarged to paste on the record jacket. It is still one of his prized possessions which he will play for guests with no encouragement at all. I know I couldn't have pleased him more if I had given him a Silver Cloud Rolls!

To me, one of the most beautiful descriptions of marriage I have ever read was written by the famed poet, philosopher, and mystic, Kahlil Gibran. Included in his classic work, *The Prophet*, are the following words:

Love one another, but make not a bond of love....

More beautifully than I've ever seen it expressed, the poet explains that married people don't own each other. They are not "as one" but rather "together."

OLD YOU feels boredom is inevitable in marriage. She's willing to talk about how bored she is with her friends but is unwilling to do anything constructive.

NEW YOU fights boredom as she would bedbugs. A boring atmosphere affects the entire household, including children, dogs, and goldfish. She is the nerve-center of the marriage. If her nerve-endings are allowed to go dead, the atmosphere disintegrates into that of a busy, but impersonal bus station.

OLD YOU thinks what happened to her all day is the dullest thing that ever happened.

NEW YOU recognizes the home and her role in it as a touchstone of continuity in her husband's life. She thinks about what he's doing and one part of her consciousness is with him all the time. If he was going to an important meeting, she remembers to ask him what happened. If he was making a speech, playing in a tournament, stopping off at the doctor's, she doesn't wait for him to bring it up and then say, "Oh, yes, I forgot!" She remembers!

OLD YOU is impatient with her husband's sports, enthusiasms and hobbies and throws cold water on his pet projects with little whines of "It's so expensive!"

Unless, of course, his hobbies or pet projects are female, NEW YOU tries to see things as her husband sees them and cheer him on even if from the sidelines. Whether he's ga-ga over stamp collecting, jazz, growing a beard, or driving a red sportscar *at his age?*—the least critical audience should be the home audience.

OLD YOU thinks being a wife means that you stop being a woman.

NEW YOU realizes that a woman, like Gaul, is divided into three parts: wife, mother, mistress. When I was sixteen, with dreams of being a writer, and was a student at the Nardin Academy in Buffalo, N. Y., I wrote a short story about a man who received three letters, one from his mother, one from his wife, one from his girl friend. Each had something different to say to him, a different way of describing her love and her place in his life. At the end of the story, I revealed that all three letters were from the same woman, his wife.

If you're all three to your husband, you're everything he could ever want or hope to have—and you *are* a woman.

OLD YOU prides herself that she is only interested in one man, her husband, and "never looks at another man!"

NEW YOU looks, listens, and learns from talking to and mingling with men of all ages. At parties, community events, wherever she happens to be, she really pays attention to older men, grandfathers, teenage boys who mow the lawn, her husband's friends, her friends' husbands. As every career woman knows, being and working with men is stimulating. It takes you out of your female vacuum. If you can be interested in and interesting to men on a casual, informal basis, think how devastating you can be to your very own man.

Have you made up your mind? Are you going to take a man away from his wife?

Scarlett O'Hara made a point of thinking about things "tomorrow," and she was left at the end trying to figure out how she was going to get Rhett Butler to come back.

Break up the old marriage, by all means. Wake up the new marriage, by every means possible.

Set yourself a deadline. The best place to grab a husband is in the home. Your own home. Take your husband away from the *OLD YOU*.

It's only a chapter in a book—but I know lots of people to whom I wish I could have said these things. It's worth a try—anyway, it may save you from a lot of lonely hours!

How to Have Beautiful Hair Without Marrying Your Hairdresser

Your hair is the first thing a man notices. You could be wearing open-toe galoshes with a gold lamé snowsuit, and because one strand of hair is out of place, the first thing he says is, "What happened to your head? Get caught in the mix-master?"

Your hairstyle is your most important single outward sign of personal identity. Proof of this is the quickie description commonly heard.

"You know—the wild redhead!"

"Who is that dynamic-looking blonde?"

"So I went out last night with this dark-haired, Mediterranean type."

You have also heard, "What's that on her head—a floor mop?"

To paraphrase the *Ladies Home Journal*'s ad campaign, "Never underestimate the womanly power of beautiful hair."

As beauty expert Gaylord Hauser said, "I believe there is no other single feature that can do so much for a woman's looks as a mass of sweet-smelling, shining hair. Also, there is no feminine feature that can glamorize, minimize or balance facial shortcomings as can beautiful hair. In the same way that a good frame brings out and highlights a picture, just so can beautiful hair frame and highlight an almost beautiful face into extraordinary beauty."

Lovely hair appeals to several of the basic senses. Its glorious texture and color highlights are a feast to the eyes. Its texture and liveliness of movement are an invitation to the touch. Its clean, shiny healthiness sends out a subtle perfume that is enticing to the sensitive nose.

The roots of hair beauty are simple: good health and good care. If you have crummy clumps of wheat sprouting from your scalp, you can have Alexandre of Paris, Vidal Sassoon, Kenneth, George Masters and my own Antoine working on your head from now until Sunday and it will help—but not much.

Dull, limp lifeless hair is a tragedy for a woman. A few strokes of a hairbrush and some honeyed words from me aren't going to change things overnight. But if this is your tragedy, you can't start on it a moment too soon.

The most important factor in beautiful hair is that thing called "body" which describes the thickness and strength of each hair, the flexibility and zing with which it responds to the comb and brush.

"Body" comes from the inside, not the outside. You can't rinse it in. While I hate to sound discouraging, it may take a while to restore hair health. Don't delay—and if you are really miserable about the looks of your hair, get to work at once on nursing it back to health. Instead of torturing yourself with disappointing hair-sets, wear fashion wigs all the time instead of just for special occasions, until you're ready to stick your bare head out in public again.

Since your lady Eve studied journalism at college and not medicine, I am not about to hang out my shingle and prescribe dermatology treatments for your hair. If you have noticed a dramatic deterioration in hair health—hair falling out, ends breaking off, total lifelessness and resistance to setting

—I would urgently recommend you see a doctor or dermatologist or you may be a candidate for the Yul Brynner Award for Hair Loveliness.

If you are merely dissatisfied with hair which you *know* could look better, I do have some diet suggestions which are fundamental to healthy hair. I'm not telling tales out of medical school when I say carbonated drinks, excessively oily foods like peanuts and potato chips, overly sweet desserts, candies, and snacks have an adverse effect on the sebaceous glands and the hair follicles.

Cutting down on these things is a big step forward. While excluding the bad stuff, you must also make a special effort to include the good stuff for hair health, including lots of protein such as lean meat, fish, eggs, cottage cheese and generous amounts of whole-grain bread, fruit juices and honey.

Your body goes limp without exercise. The same goes for your hair. Brushing the hair is like giving it a massage. Brushing stimulates the scalp and distributes your own natural hair oils through each strand of hair.

As a model said to me one day during a fashion show, "Brushing feels so good. It makes my scalp come alive and after a few minutes of brushing, my hair seems to do whatever I want it to do."

More and more, I see models and career girls carrying a hairbrush around with them in their handbags or totes. One secretary told me, "I never use a comb anymore. I simply brush my hair into place. Since I've started using a hairbrush, I find my hair is more manageable, easier to prod into position."

Here I would like to say two things about hairbrushes:

One, natural-bristle brushes are good but so are nylon bristles. Frequently, I read admonitions about natural bristles as the only safeguard to hair. This is an old-fashioned idea that goes back to the early days of nylon when nylon bristles *were* harsh and *did* lacerate the head. Today's nylon brushes offer as many gradations of stiffness and softness as natural bristles —and since much of the old supply of natural bristles came from China, nylon costs a lot less than bristle. You can lose your brush in the ladies room at the restaurant without having a nervous breakdown.

Two, keep your brushes clean. Develop your own techniques. Carrying them around, many models wrap the brush in a scarf or keep it in a separate little zip bag. Most are too lazy and just dump the brush in with everything else and wash it every night.

The simplest way to have clean brushes is to toss them into a sinkful of mild detergent suds while taking your bath or shower. By the time you're clean, they're clean. With two brushes, one efficiently drags hairs off the other. Towel off the excess moisture and let them dry.

As for hair cleanliness, that's where I turn into a fanatic. I AM A NUT ABOUT CLEAN HAIR! Unless you're lucky enough to live in a pine forest miles away from industry or on a rocky storm-tossed island with a dreamy lighthouse keeper, you are exposed daily to what I call Hair Pollution. Hair Pollution is all the junk in the air that hasn't gotten into your eyes, nose, throat, lungs, and slipcovers because it has settled into your hair. Particles of soot, grime, dust, and car exhaust have a cute way of creating a film that penetrates your hair. You can fight hair pollution by fighting for Air Pollution legislation in your area—and by washing your hair as often as necessary.

I don't believe in absolute rules about hair-washing. As much as I adore and admire Gaylord Hauser and other experts who believe every two weeks is often enough, I think you should shampoo as often as you feel it necessary.

Actually, Hauser's advice goes back to the days when soaps and shampoos removed the hair's natural oils as well as the dirt. Today, however, the new shampoos include restorative oils and conditioning agents that revitalize the hair as they clean.

While disagreeing with the famous Gaylord on this one point, I heartily concur with his views on the health aspects of hair. His book, *Mirror, Mirror on the Wall*, should stand on every woman's bedside bookshelf. My favorite Hair-care Cocktail is his "Toast to Your Crowning Glory."

Into a cup of lean or skim milk, add a tablespoon of pure gelatin, a teaspoon of sesame oil, and a teaspoon of honey, molasses or fruit flavor. As Gaylord Hauser explains, adding milk to gelatin doubles its potency. This pleasant cocktail provides vitamin B, calcium, protein and the fatty acids of sesame oil that combat hair dryness.

Hair spray is another thing that turns me into a snarling tigress. I am not a violent woman, but every time I see a woman empty a half-gallon can of spray on her head, I am overwhelmed with a mild wish to break her arm. Or at least knock the spray can out of her hand.

It's not that I don't believe in hair spray. I do, but in moderation. After all, the Eve Nelson products which I designed include hair spray. I think every woman should use it to good advantage. I don't want a year's supply of hair spray to be used in three weeks. My accountant might like it, but I wouldn't.

The function of hair spray is to add a gossamer veil of holding power to your set, to add an extra glimmer of sheen to your already shiny hair, to help tame recalcitrant locks and to give a smidgin of extra "body."

Hair spray should not take the place of setting or styling. If you douse your hair with spray and then "glue" the style into place, you not only look like a department store dummy, but when you put a comb to your hair, watch out!

Those of us over twenty-five (okay, over thirty-five) may tend to copy the teenagers who seem to make a religious ritual of hair spray. I wish the kids would take it easy for the sake of their own hair. But I will point out one thing. Teenagers' hair is naturally strong and healthy with the oils of youth. They can get away with more hair spray at their age. The grown-up woman's hair lacks the elasticity and strength of the very young. Think of hair spray as you would garlic. A little goes a long, long way.

What You Should Know About Styling

HOW TO SET YOUR OWN HAIR

Yes, you love going to the hairdresser. It's a luxurious interlude, a time-out-of-time of self-beautification when you can forget the outside world and surrender yourself to the ministering hands of the experts.

Still, there are times when you can't get to the hairdresser. There are emergencies after a day on the ski slopes or in the summer sea when you have to "do something about your hair." If you have a well-styled haircut, shaped to fall into place and suit the contours of your face—setting your hair is a simple matter of mastering a few basic techniques:

1. Have rollers in several sizes so you can vary your setting as desired.

2. Don't run out of clips, bobby pins or other necessaries. Keep them in a small plastic see-through box where you keep your rollers.

3. Keep a roll of tape handy for pasting down bangs or cheek curls you want to dry flat.

4. Don't wait until you've wet your hair to discover you're out of shampoo. A good rule is to get a new supply every time you start a new bottle or tube.

5. After a shampoo, towel-dry hair and comb through.

6. Apply setting lotion and comb through.

7. Follow setting diagrams carefully.

8. Be sure hair is completely dry before brushing out the set. AND DON'T BE AFRAID TO BRUSH! Brushing gives added bounce and sheen to the hair.

9. Lightly spray your finished coiffure.

The six hair styles illustrated in this section are always fashionable and are quick and easy. Arrows indicate how each style is to be set.

Fig. 4   A buoyant, definitive wave flipped upward

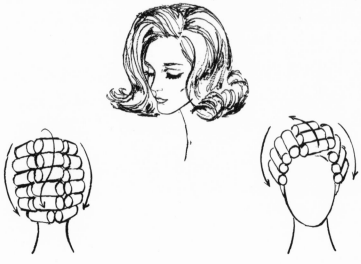

Fig. 5   *A natural look becoming to any shape face,*
any length hair

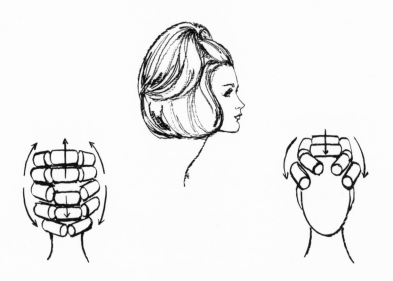

Fig. 6   *A "triangular" set, smooth and high*

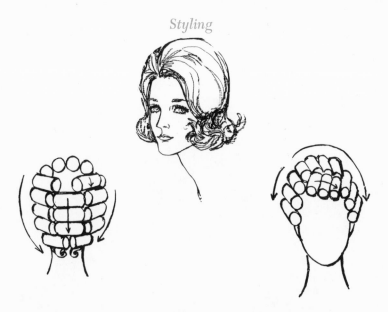

Fig. 7   A flirty-soft flip, perfect for the oval
         or square-contoured face

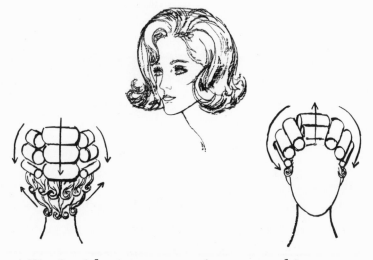

Fig. 8   A basic set to transform a round face
         or a square one into oval-sleek loveliness

93

Fig. 9   *Extremely versatile—brush it back*
to bare your ears or flip it gently forward

Hair Color Dictionary

In today's beauty picture, hair-coloring has become as much a part of the scene as lipstick and nail polish. Modern developments have perfected the techniques for color application and for keeping hair healthy and lively.

Since every specialized field develops its own vocabulary,

94

there may be times when you are confused about terms you hear at the beauty salon. To clear up this confusion and to help you discuss hair-coloring with your hairdresser, here are some of the most commonly used terms:

ash or drab–coloring which eliminates or subdues red or gold tone, by desired degree.

bleach or hair lightener–a product which lightens hair by de-coloring or removing the natural pigment. The degree of lightening can be moderate, depending on the product used.

color-filler–a preparation that is applied to hair which has been damaged or abused and, therefore, will not properly accept or retain hair-coloring.

dye–the name given to the older types of permanent hair-colorings which colored the hair darker.

lift–lightening of natural hair pigment.

oxidation colorings–those requiring the addition of hydrogen peroxide or a substitute for the development of color on the hair.

patch test or skin test–a method of determining if an individual is hypersensitive to a hair-coloring product.

porosity–the condition of the hair which enables it to accept colorings.

retouch–tinting or bleaching of the new growth.

strand test–the testing of a single strand of hair with a coloring preparation prior to treating the entire head.

stripping–removing artificial color from the hair.

tint–a permanent hair-coloring which has the ability to color gray and lighten the natural pigment simultaneously.

toner–special shades of tints or rinses that are used on highly bleached hair.

virgin hair–literally, hair which has not been bleached, tinted or permanently waved. In hair-coloring, usually hair which has not been bleached or treated with permanent color.

Sum-Up

In your quest for beautiful hair, don't lose your perspective or your sense of humor. Perspective will keep you from believing claims of many products, that one application will assure you of instant sex appeal, great wealth, and an invitation to spend the summer on a yacht. Perspective will help you judge which rituals of hair care and which products will do the most for you personally.

In fact, to stop yourself from going off on some exotic—and expensive—tangent, remember humorist Henry Morgan's remark on being told that Tibetan women rub rancid yak butter into their hair as a hairdressing. Henry thought this over for a few seconds and then said, "But what if they can't find a rancid yak?"

My final word on hair is a personal one. There's an old joke about "What's the definition of a nymphomaniac?" The answer: "The girl who lets her husband make love to her right after she's had her hair done."

In your quest for beautiful hair, don't forget that the object is to become gorgeous enough to get some man to mess it all up!

How to Get the Most Out of Your Hairdresser

Some women swear by (and sometimes at) having a male hairdresser.

"A man wants you to look your best! Psychologically, no woman really wants another woman to be beautiful!"

Other equally fervent women say that only a woman can truly understand another woman's beauty problems and that they will only trust a female stylist.

My feeling is, live and be well. This is the one area where you should play your hunches. Find the stylist with whom you can have a good, creative relationship and stick to him (or her).

For the sake of simplicity and because I like men, I will refer to the hairdresser as "he" in this section. In fact, I'm going to turn the platform over to one of the most outstandingly creative young men in hairdressing today. He is Antoine M., Creative Director of the fourteen Eve Nelson Beauty Salons. He's tall, handsome, married (sorry, girls), and not only develops new styles and techniques of setting for millions of women but trains over five hundred stylists each year.

If you're not a jet-set darling who can invite her hairdresser to go everywhere with her, then pay attention to Antoine M. who explains:

1. Wear makeup, especially eye makeup. The hairdresser is an artist who styles, shapes and sets your hair to flatter your face. He can't do his best if your "face" is left home. This is particularly important for girls with pale eyebrows and lashes whose expression disappears without the emphasis of cosmetics.

2. The first few times you go to a hairdresser, wear one of your favorite outfits and let him see you in it. The style and personality of your clothes will give him a visual

impression of you as a complete woman and not a disem-bodied head above the cotton wrapper. After you're friends and he knows you, then you can slop in wearing old blue jeans and whatever you like. But unless he has a complete image, how can he judge whether you are con-servative, mod, hippie or ultra-feminine?

3. It follows that if you want a special style created for a special occasion, take the time and trouble to bring in the dress. This is especially crucial for an engagement or wedding party. Hairstyling is created for the whole effect and not just from the neck up.

4. Try not to be rigid about preconceived ideas. If you bring in a picture cut from a magazine, understand that this gives the hairdresser an "idea" but that he cannot copy the hairdo exactly unless you have the same facial structure as the model shown.

5. When changing your hair color, be guided by the color expert at your salon. Keep in mind the optical illusion of hair coloring. Dark hair, for instance, makes a face seem much thinner than fair hair. (See opposite page.)

    Whether you decide to be dark, light, or reddish, listen to the advice of the colorist who will take into account your skin tones, the amount of gray, if any, and your own natural hair coloring.

6. Take an interest in new hairstyle trends. Ask your hair-dresser how they may be adapted to you. The smart woman learns to understand her own face and head shape and which "lines" are most suitable to her contours. That doesn't mean you have to get stuck with the same hairdo for years on end, but rather the same basic needs of height or emphasis.

    If you see the exact same shop window week after

Fig. 10

Fig. 11

week, it doesn't matter how pretty it is, you simply lose interest and stop looking.

7. Remember that faces change. You get thinner. You get plumper. You have your teeth fixed. You change your style of makeup. Your general appearance evolves slowly. Give your hairstyle the chance to do the same.

8. If you wear glasses, wear them during a styling and shaping. This way, your hairstyle can incorporate and complement your specs.

9. To talk or not to talk? Take your cue from him. It's your head that's in his hands. If he's talkative, great. You talk, too. But if he seems quiet and dreamy, don't divert him. He may be coming up with something wonderful for you.

10. Give yourself enough time to have your hair done properly. The Rush Act only defeats the purpose of going to the hairdresser. If you're nervous and fretful, it infects him, too, and if he feels harassed, it's bound to affect your comb-out.

11. If he wants to try something brand new—take a chance —let him. Your hairdresser is a creative artist who is always working to achieve new techniques for making you more beautiful. In the long run, you are the one who benefits. You may not "love" the new style, but then again, it may be so becoming, it will change your life! You can't know unless you try.

12. Your hairdresser can be one of the most important men in your life. If he "understands" you and you feel a continuing confidence in him, make the gestures of friendship to him as you do toward your other friends. On a trip, send a picture postcard to him at the salon. All hairdressers love being remembered by clients. Send Christmas cards and birthday cards, too, if you happen to know

the latter. A small remembrance at Christmas is always well received and makes the stylist feel appreciated.

13. If you barge in unexpectedly for a comb-out, don't make a Liz Taylor scene to be fitted in that very instant. A tantrum may lose you the services of those magic hands forever.

14. Be on time for appointments. *Please.*

The devotion of hairdressers to their art and to their ladies is nicely expressed by Mr. Sal, Managing Director of the Eve Nelson salons. Mr. Sal was brought up in the beauty business and has known literally thousands of hair stylists at various stages of their careers. If there's one man in the country who knows all about hairdressers, from behind the scenes, it's our Mr. Sal.

"Hairdressers are totally dedicated to their ladies, at any salon," he said. "They worry about their regular customers and feel a deep sense of loyalty. You wouldn't believe it but I've seen one of our stylists get out of a sick bed to take care of a lady who needed his services."

"Once," he recalled, "one of our men was on vacation. A woman who had been coming to him for years suddenly called in a panic. She was going to a fancy opening at the opera and was desperate. You know what that man did? He jumped into his car and drove all the way in from the country so that his lady would look beautiful!"

Mr. Sal loves the beauty business, as do I, and as new people join the expanding Eve Nelson salons, he teaches them the rewards of loyalty and personal concern for the customer. We know how you feel if you go to a beauty salon for the first time and leave disappointed because you and one operator didn't quite communicate. There were probably eight other stylists who would have been divine for you! Seek and you shall find the one right for you.

The hair stylist is part of your life because what he gives you is an extension of his talented hands and creative art.

How to Completely Change Your Appearance in Wig-time

There is a primitive excitement about wearing a fashion hairpiece that goes back to the beginning of recorded time. The ancient Egyptians wore them, men and women alike. If you saw the movie, *Cleopatra,* you may have had your eyes riveted to Richard Burton most of the time, but you must have noticed Liz Taylor's hair, a series of magnificent wigs in the style of the Queen of the Nile.

In the ancient Greek theater, the color of the player's wig instantly denoted character: black for villains and tyrants, blonde curls for the hero or heroine, red for the comic.

Certain Orthodox Jewish sects, from the beginning of Judaism right up to today, oblige married women to wear wigs on the assumption that a woman's own hair is too seductive to be seen by any man except her husband. These wigs were supposed to be patently artificial and unbecoming but, even among the very pious moderns, women are seeking a fashionable color and shape under which to hide their tresses.

My view of fashion hairpieces is simple: I couldn't live without them. I don't know how I managed before they became popular. They're among the best things to happen to women since the invention of Men.

I got my first hairpiece because I talk too much! It was about five years ago. Warren and I were getting ready for a trip to Paris. I was having my hair bleached at the salon, but because there was so much to do before we left, I was on the phone, talking business while all the little chemicals were doing their job on my hair.

The colorist kept saying, "Time's up. You'll be over-bleached," but I had seven or eight thousand more things to say—and believe me they *were* important—and by the time he wrenched me away from the phone, I was over-bleached.

"You're going to have problems," he predicted, running a comb through my short blonde hair.

"It's all my fault!" I reassured him. That fact didn't improve my disposition when my hair started to break off and I began to look like a sheared raccoon.

It was at that moment, dear friends, that I realized I had a choice of going to Paris, France, with my head in a paper bag or hide the disaster under some fashion hairpieces. I quickly got a full fashion wig plus a wiglet cluster of curls in my own blonde shade.

The trip was fabulous and my "hair" won me plenty of ooh-la-las. For me, it became a whole other way of living a busy life. My own hair grew back and bounced back to its usual healthy state. Yet, I now own a wardrobe of fashion pieces consisting of two wigs, a fall, and a wiglet in my own blonde, plus a sultry, dark wig for fun or "disguise." I keep them all in a state of readiness for a quick trip or an elegant evening after a rainy day when my hair behaves as if it belongs to someone else.

The only time a wig ever gave me trouble was one day on Fifth Avenue. I was steaming along at one hundred miles an hour, looking in store windows to see what they had that our store didn't, and battling a brisk March wind when suddenly—my wig flew off! Did you ever chase your hair down the street?

A friend of mine in Houston was dying to get a wig for the longest time but her husband didn't want her to have it. Finally, she ordered one on the q.t. I happened to be in Houston the day she went to pick it up. Was she nervous!

"How can I wear it home? He'll kill me."

I convinced her to wear it home. He wouldn't kill her, all he might do was lock her out of the house but this didn't seem likely.

She wore the wig home. Most married women probably can guess what happened next. Nothing. Her husband didn't notice it. Was she furious!

"I'm wearing a wig!" she burst out. "Can't you tell?"

The happy ending was her husband was delighted. He thought she looked marvelous.

"When you said *wig* I was afraid you were going to look like Harpo Marx," he said.

What You Should Know About Fashion Hairpieces

What's the difference between Oriental and European hair?

Oriental hair comes from Korea, Japan, Vietnam, and other parts of Asia, with the exception of Red China (because of trade restrictions). The individual hairs are shaped differently from European hair. The roots of Oriental hair are round, European hair has roots that taper into spear-like papillae.

Because of the hair shape, Oriental hair can be made into a hairpiece from either end and will take a set. European hair must be fastened to a wig or wiglet foundation by the root ends. Otherwise, the hair is upside down and resists sets and brushing.

Oriental hair is coarser than the silkier European. It is also easier to set, holds the setting longer and is more adaptable to the straight-hair styling many women seek.

European hair tends to be silky. Despite stories of nuns cutting off their hair for the hair buyers, the bulk of the European hair is "combed" rather than cut. Women of small villages in Italy, Spain, and France "comb" their long hair from the scalp and collect it in boxes. In rural Italian mountain regions, they use spaghetti boxes.

Whatever the origin of the hair, its real color is unimportant. Whether the hair came from an ebony-haired Korean or a blonde North Italian, all hair is bleached bone white in the wig-making process.

If my hairpiece is one color, can I have it dyed another color?

It is not advisable to dye human hair fashion hairpieces. Once hair has been made into an accessory, it is no longer nourished by the natural oil of the body. After the initial dying process, additional use of tinting chemicals may weaken or dull the hair. You have a fair chance of success if you dye a lighter-shade wig darker. Trying to bleach a darker wig light is asking for trouble.

What's the difference between a hand-made and machine-made hairpiece?

Turn the hairpiece inside out. If each hair is attached to the net foundation with a double knot that you can barely see, it's probably hand-made. If there are rows of stitching or any indication of circular sewing, the piece was made by machine.

Obviously, there's a big difference in price between hand-mades and machine-mades. Oddly enough, the best machine-made wig is, for most women, a better choice than a hand-made. Apart from the difference in cost which may run into the hundreds of dollars, a machine-made hairpiece generally has more body strength and holds the set better. The hand-mades tend to be more fragile and require more tender loving care.

Is there a difference between custom-blended and custom-made?

Yes, for a custom-blend, the hairpiece is blended to exactly match a sample of your own hair. This is especially important in the choice of a wiglet or fall which must match the rest of your hair that shows. For a full wig, you might select a shade near but not quite identical to your own from a color wheel of hair swatches.

The custom-blend hairpiece is then shaped and styled by your hairdresser to fit your head and conform to the contours of your face. While the color is customized, the hairpiece itself is generally machine-sewn on one of many standard foundations, depending on your needs.

A custom-made hairpiece, however, is created for you and you alone, from the foundation out. Your exact head measurements are taken. The hair is dyed to specification, hand-knotted one hair at a time, and fastened into the foundation. Cutting and styling follow.

How many types of hairpieces are there?

There are seven major types:

the full wig–designed to cover your entire head, it may be styled like your own hair or into an elaborate coif for a special event when super-elegance is your goal.

the switch–a hank of hair from about twelve to twenty inches long, most frequently attached to the crown of the head and worn loose and mingled with your own hair, clipped on in a floppy ponytail, or braided or coiled in any number of styles. (See Figure 12.)

Fig. 12

Fig. 13

the wiglet–a length of hair usually about twelve inches long that is woven into a net base. The base shape may be oval, triangular or circular. Its size depends on which part of the head you intend to anchor it—top, back, or sides. Most wiglets are attached on top with a comb sewn into the base. When choosing a wiglet, be sure the hair is thick and can be combed in all directions without gaps or separation. (See Figure 13.)

the fall–probably the most practical hairpiece design, it is best described as a semi-wig. The thick length of hair ranges in length from eighteen to twenty-eight inches and is attached to a net base that spans the top of the head like a hairband. The hair is woven to "fall" back over your own hair. (See Figure 14.)

Fig. 14

the demi-wig–ideal for those with thin or lank hair that is a problem to set. The demi-wig is actually a very short wig with bangs that fits over and blends into your own hair so that both are visible. (See Figure 15.)

Fig. 15

the bangs caplet–another short wig for those who like bangs, with longer strands of hair at the temples to produce a Joan of Arc cap-cut effect. (See Figure 16.)

Fig. 16

Fig. 17

bangs and *curls*–food for the imagination, bangs that match your own hair and attach with a small comb so you can have a forehead fringe at will; a cluster of curls to achieve a romantic style for a gala evening by simply pinning them on. (See Figure 17.)

Are there some pointers for putting on hairpieces?

To attach your fall or wiglet, place two large pincurls of your own hair just underneath the spot where the hairpiece will start. Cross the pincurls with bobby pins. A comb is sewn into the net base of the hairpiece. Insert this comb under the pincurls which will anchor it. For extra height on the crown, pull the top part of your hair into a rubber band. This will give you some bulk under the hairpiece.

To attach your switch, pull your own hair into a rubber band at the exact point where the switch will be anchored. Secure the switch with bobby pins. Blend the switch and your own hair together into the desired hairstyle.

What about cleaning a hairpiece?

Do not wet it. *Repeat.* Do not ever, ever, *ever* put water on human hair hairpieces. If you think your own hair is unmanageable when it gets wet, you don't know what trouble is until you try to untangle the matted floor-mop that results from washing a hairpiece.

If you're a clever girl, clean your hairpiece at home. Use only a hairpiece cleaner made specifically for the purpose and *follow the directions—including the small print.* Usually this is a messy job of swishing the hair strands through the cleanser, holding the base free from the liquid. Do not wring or twist. Allow excess cleaner fluid to drip off. Press out excess in a clean towel. Dry by pinning to your head block.

If you're *not* a clever girl, why risk wrecking your lovely hair accessories? Take good care of them by brushing and combing them free of dust and soot. When they finally do get dirty, have them cleaned professionally by your hairdresser. This way, you're certain of success.

What's the best way to take care of a hairpiece?

A head-block is a good investment. Attach your hairpiece to it with T-pins. This way, you can work out tangles with a large hairpin and gently brush and comb the tresses, too.

Between wearings keep a full wig on a wig-stand, covered with a silk scarf to protect it from dust while allowing air to circulate around it—and also to keep your husband from being scared to death by Marie Antoinette's ghost.

Your switch should be brushed free of tangles, twisted into a loose coil and wrapped in a thin scarf.

Your fall keeps its shape best if wrapped around a cardboard tube (an ordinary two-inch mailing tube works fine), and then rolled into a silk scarf.

Is it possible to set your own hairpiece?

Unless you are especially adept, you should have a full wig set by the hairdresser only. A wiglet or fall is easier to handle, so why not give it a whirl—but treat it gently. Attach the hairpiece to your wig-block with T-pins. Use wire rollers in order to allow air to pass through. Anchor each roller with a single three-inch bobby pin or hair grip. Use as few bobby pins as possible since hairpiece hair marks easily. *Do not use setting lotion. Do* use a minimum of tepid water on the fingertips to dampen hair strands. Allow to dry naturally.

Take it from Eve:

You may have noticed an omission in this chapter. I have not discussed synthetic hairpieces. My reason is, I consider synthetics as a fashion category quite separate from hairpieces. Just as I love hats, I adore dynel and nylon switches and braids for appropriate uses with sportswear, on the beach and for achieving a special party effect.

A recent fashion advertising campaign for coats said, "This isn't fake anything; it's real dynel." Synthetic hair fashions are in the same category. They should not be worn as fakery but as real accessories in their own right.

Beauty Makes the Most of the Machine Age

The beauty machines are changing our lives.

These days, when the phone rings, you don't say, "Hang on while I turn off the vacuum cleaner." Instead, it's more likely to be, "Wait t-t-till I t-t-turn off my v-v-vibrator!"

Suddenly, the kids are brushing their teeth all day long with electric toothbrushes. Steamers, massagers, exercisers, relaxers are giving salon excitement to the average home. Husbands are loving it. Teenagers are finding it groovy. The lady of the house is discovering the miracles of plug-in beauty at the flip of a switch.

It's a little bit like having your own beauty club at home. When I was growing up, my daydreams of luxury living were a combination of princess and movie star. I could visualize myself in a pink satin setting with my gorgeous husband—and, in the background, a resident hairdresser, cosmetologist, masseuse, and dietician, all hanging around waiting for Madame to snap her fingers (or whistle).

Wouldn't that have been great? *Quick, Mario—my massage!*

As a busy woman with a seventy-four-hour day, you've probably had the same daydream. Before we join hands in mourning for the loss of this dream, let me point out that the dream isn't really lost. It has come true—but on modern terms.

In today's smaller living space, there's no room for a live-in masseuse but there *is* room for the hair dryer, the vibrators, the facial sauna. Complain as we may about machines replacing elevator operators and at food counters, in the field of home beauty, the machines are doing jobs that have never been done before.

Soon, every American home will be wired for beauty. All you will have to do is plug yourself in to feel better and look better—and no tipping!

Maybe it sounds silly to think of machines for beauty, but it shouldn't. Think how machines have changed your domestic life. Grinders, blenders, mixers, toasters, and roasters in the kitchen. Polishers, sweepers, purifiers and Lord-knows-what-else for the rest of the house. What about you? If machines can prolong the life and beauty of the living room upholstery, think what they can do for yours.

Currently my favorite beauty machine is the face sauna. It's the up-to-date version of the old towel-over-the-head steam process our grandmothers taught us. What a mess that used to be! Now, all you do is close your eyes and feel the lovely steam cleaning and reviving your poor, tired face.

In fact, the whole concept of sauna bathing has become so popular in America that the prices are coming down to meet the demand. I used to think the only people who had a sauna at home were rich folks and Swedes. In getting price estimates for installing saunas in our Eve Nelson salons, I found the costs to be much lower than I thought.

Country clubs have begun to install them. In many suburban communities, groups of four or five couples share the cost of putting one into a basement or garage. Even city dwellers are finding ways to install a modest-sized or portable sauna in an apartment.

To give you some idea of what's going on in the beauty-machine market, here's an informal round-up.

Start with Your Body

You remember. Your body! All those acres of skin, all those lovely bones you tend to ignore until they remind you by showing signs of wear and tear or pain!

You've seen garage machanics fuss over the body work of a car. Because you can't trade in *your* chassis, make it your beauty business to keep it sleek and purring. There are all kinds of fabulous machines to help you relax, sleep and improve your figure.

There are body exercisers which make you look like a creature from Mars with all kinds of pads strapped onto your body. While you relax, the pads firm and tone problem areas of the body and are great for spot-reducing.

There's a belt massager which makes me feel like an old-style shimmy dancer. *Quick, Mario, my tango records.* It shakes all the kinks out while exercising and firming flabby hips and thighs.

Exercycles get you into the habit of pedaling a few miles a day, a good workout for legs, abdomen, neck and back—and no worries about traffic!

In checking around for approximate prices, I find that body exerciser prices go from about $100 to $450; belt massagers range from $35 to $110; and exercycles, $10 to $25.

The vibrators these days are so terrific that you may get hooked on them and never leave the house. There are small, hand vibrators that enable you to massage your own scalp, legs and hips—get the man in your life to do your neck, shoulders and back. Deep-heat massagers can soothe the aches of arthritis, aching muscles, and tensions.

Remember those curved neck rests? Now, they're available with a built-in vibrator to ease stiff necks that plague so many busy people. Keep this in mind for your husband if he works bent over a desk. The curve of the pillow also fits around a thigh or arm for gentle massage.

If you want to vibrate, honey, there are even more marvelous inventions in the stores: a vibrating slant board that gives you the double benefits of slant positions plus massage; a vibrating back rest you can use for watching TV, working at a desk, or reading in bed; a vibrating wedge pillow that also doubles your comfort by supplying back support plus massage action.

Prices in this category go from about $10 to $40 for hand vibrators, $14 for neck rests, $30 for slant boards, and $20 for a large wedge pillow.

As for a sauna bath, the increased popularity has inspired manufacturers to bring out a variety of styles so that everyone can afford one. There's a portable "steam bath" style for under $25. There's a compact unit you can put in a large bathroom or elsewhere in the house. There's no wiring or construction work involved. You just plug it in—for about $700. Between the two extremes is a fiberglass molded sauna cabinet for about $275 which, when you think about it, is what you might spend to take the family away for a weekend.

Of course, one of the oldest—and cheapest—body beauty

aides is the old vinyl exercise suit. It turns into a kind of walking steam bath as you do your household chores and sets you back about $5!

GLORIOUS SLEEP

A friend says the only kind of sleep machine that would do her any good is a boxing glove attached to a lever that would knock her unconscious.

There are better and sweeter ways than a right to the jaw to send you snoozing. Naturally, the vibrating and massaging devices mentioned above are relaxing and soothing and will help you to sleep better. In addition, there's an army of designers staying awake nights, dreaming up bed accessories for inducing rest.

There's a mattress elevator which fits under your mattress and raises it to whatever height you want, just like one of those hospital beds, about $13. There are folding backrests, about $6; bed boards, about $8; foam wedges in all sizes and contours, from $10 to $20.

If you live in a cold climate and wake up exhausted every morning, think about an electric blanket. It gives you the warmth without the weight of a mountain of blankets crushing your fragile, tender frame. Prices from $15 to $50.

BATHING BEAUTY

Health farms have them. Beauty spas have them. The fancier salons charge you an arm and a leg for one session—and then you have to get dressed and go home.

What I'm talking about are the hydro-therapy attachments you can use in your own private bathtub. The churning, whirling water gives you a relaxing, soothing massage to relieve stiffness and tension. It peps up circulation, makes your skin feel alive and zingy, so you practically leap out of the tub like a runaway fawn. (Be careful, no toe dancing, or you may slip.) Prices range from $40 to $200.

A bath accessory many women love is one of the waterproof bath pillows. You attach it to the wall or the back of the tub with suction cups. It cushions your head and keeps it dry while you loll in the comfort of your warm bath. Under $5.

FACE SAVERS

More than any other part of you, your face takes all the stings and blows of outrageous fortune. Dirt, soot, air pollution, fatigue all attack the face. You can ward off damage with one of the many types of facial sauna now on the market. It's one of the nicest beauty treatments I know. A pleasant, warm steam bathes your complexion like a loving mist. It cleanses the pores, refreshes the skin texture, and leaves you with a dewy glow. Some of the new electric hair dryers come with a facial sauna attachment, so if you're thinking about a new hair dryer, you might explore this. Facial saunas start at about $15.

Another face machine is a facial exerciser that operates on the principles of isometric exercise. That is, it doesn't vibrate or give off heat. Instead, it gently stimulates the face and neck muscles that may be starting to sag and helps forestall wrinkles. About $70.

It's surprising how many young women suffer from facial neuralgia, sinus headaches, stiff necks or strained eyes—any one of which could make Jean Shrimpton look haggard. There are many inexpensive ways to ease these problems and prevent the lines and wrinkles they create.

There are facial masks and eye masks that exude deep, penetrating heat without the bother of hot water bags or facecloths. Under $10. There are masks you can make icy cold to give you the relief of an ice pack without fiddling in the freezer. About $3. There's a tie-on collar that concentrates dry heat on the nerve center at the back of your neck, easing stiffness and ache. Under $10. In fact, a friend of mine frequently wears hers in the kitchen, plugged in above her work counter where she prepares dinner.

"I just have to be careful not to get the cord wet."

HAIR REPAIR

These days, there's no excuse for walking around like Ma Kettle! The old excuses for sloppy-looking hair simply don't stand up to examination.

You have young children and can't get to the hairdresser? Your husband has asked you to join him for a business dinner and your hair appointment isn't until Saturday? You never have time for your hair during the day and there's no all-night hairdresser where you live?

Get some new excuses—or get some of the home hair-care machinery that is fast becoming as much a part of domestic equipment as the toaster. We creaking old-timers can thank the teenagers for boosting the design of home hair dryers and other beauty gadgets. The kids want them so the manufacturers make them—and all of us benefit.

In fact, the girls went so wacky over plug-in equipment, many colleges have had to put a limit on the number of electric items each student may bring to the dormitory because the wiring can take just so much!

The portable hair dryer is by far the best thing that ever happened in home beauty. Now that the men are wearing their hair thicker and longer, many women are luring their husbands under the dryer to speed up drying and to prevent colds.

Most of the dryers fold up compactly for storage when not in use. If you have the room, there are standing floor dryers like the ones in the beauty salon that roll out of the way into a corner or closet. Prices range from $4.95 for a portable to $60 for the professional type.

For refreshing a set and for travel, many young women today use the new quick-heat hair rollers. There are several variations on the market. All you do is heat them up, stick them in your hair and ten minutes later, you've restored your set. Prices from under $5 for the kind you put in hot water to $30 or $40 for the electrically heated.

Other quick-set and quick-dry items include an electric "hot comb" that blows hot air on the strands of hair as you tease or style. Under $5. There's a travel dryer shaped like a gun that can blast hot air on your rollers or dry your manicure. This latter isn't a substitute for a regular hair dryer but it is useful for weekends or emergency spot-drying of bangs or a flip. It is priced at about $5.

If you are like me and wear hats and wigs a lot, you may be gypping your scalp of needed air and circulation. I use the hand massagers and vibrators discussed earlier in the chapter because they are also useful for scalp massage and stirring up those follicles.

GOING ALL OUT ON YOUR LIMBS

Don't think your arms and legs have been neglected. Electric manicure sets can give you a professional manicure and pedicure. You'll find lovely power-driven nail files, buffers, and shapers to groom the nails, remove cuticles, and prepare the surfaces for a smooth coat of polish. (All the better for palm reading!) From $10 to $30.

For tired feet, you have a choice of machines. There's a dry foot vibrator that sends thrilling little waves of relaxation through your feet while you sit at a desk or work table and struggle to balance your checkbook. About $8. There's a neat, portable hydro-therapy foot bath that circulates gallons of turbulent water around your tootsies. And when your toes begin to feel like tap-dancing, there's nothing to stop you from dunking your tired hands, wrists, and forearms into the churning water, as well. About $200.

We all know that tired legs feel better when you put them up. Don't try to be a martyr by staying on your feet for six years without rest. Explore the wide range of foot rests and leg rests that friendly designers have made. Otherwise, stick your feet up on the coffee table!

SMILE-MAKERS

Oral Hygiene may sound like a very clean Evangelist but it is the key to a sweet-tasting mouth and a healthy, gleaming smile. Since dentists don't make house calls, it's up to you to use some of the dental gadgets that have been adapted for consumer use.

As I mentioned earlier, kids really love the electric toothbrush. It's great for young teeth and protects the vitality of older teeth, especially if you have fillings or caps or other fancy dental magic—and who doesn't?

While the electric toothbrush cleans and massages, the water pik sends a jet stream of water or liquid dentrifice along the gums and between the teeth to flush out food particles the brush can't reach. The force of the water hardens the gums, makes them look healthier and feel better.

A variation is a dental spray you simply attach to the water faucet for similar cleansing and massage.

Here, the costs are very low. Everything mentioned can be purchased for less than $20. The whole family can use them and, in the long run, think what you'll save on dentist bills.

MALE-SOOTHERS

Best for last—the beauty makers of the machine age can give aid and comfort to the man in your life. Amid the tensions and competition of today's world, your husband can get a lot of pleasure and a great deal of physical good from steam treatments, vibrators and other exercise machines.

Men adore gadgets. They love mechanical "toys." While they may resist being "babied," it's a sure bet any man will be intrigued by the mechanical aspects of massage, heat and relaxation.

One of my friends swears a sauna bath saved her marriage!

She and her husband skipped a winter vacation to pay for it. "Now, we have a little vacation every day right in our own home."

Instead of drinking a few martinis in order to relax at the end of a harrowing day, her husband dives into the sauna when he gets home from work and comes out ready to wrestle a lion! "I never have to drag him to parties, anymore," she said. "Now, he drags me!"

There used to be a saying, "A man is as good as his tools." We can add, "A woman can be more beautiful and create beauty around her if she learns to use the available tools."

Beauty has made the most of the machine age. Why don't you?

Heavenly Bodies &
Tell-tale Hands

Astrology

When I first became interested in astrology, friends would react with the comment: "Are you nuts or something?"

When I branched out to palm-reading and handwriting analysis, they thought I had gone completely over the edge and was ready for basket-weaving at the funny farm.

All I can say is, some girls get their kicks out of canning string beans, some seek revelation in embroidering doorknob covers. Personally, I get my biggest charge out of people and why they are the way they are, act the way they act, and do the things they do.

Don't get me wrong. I don't believe in astrology, handwriting analysis, and adjacent arts as a substitute for religion or as a philosophy by which to live one's life. What I do feel is that each of us is a creature of nature and our own will. We are each affected by the weather, by the temperature, and by the position of the moon, so it seems logical to me that the forces of nature would have some bearing on our birth.

It is a fact that the static position of the planets at the moment of birth influences the characteristics with which you are born. This influence can be positive or dormant. It doesn't govern our total destiny since this is affected by environment, circumstance, and, of course, the signs and characters of everyone around us.

Our palms and handwriting are signs of ourselves and how we are getting along amid the pressures and pleasures of life. Just as you can tell a lot about someone by how he talks, sits, eats, and smiles, so can you see signs of character and emotion in palms and handwriting.

Most important of all—it's fun!

I'll repeat that! Astrology, palmistry, handwriting, ouija boards, E.S.P.—in fact, all attempts at revelation and communication are *fun!* It's fascinating to learn about your own birth sign. It's intriguing to know a little bit about other birth signs. In business, at parties, on trips, horoscopes give you a sudden burst of great rapport with others. After all, everybody was born! Think how fascinating you become when you can discuss a man's birth sign and what this *means*. Believe it or not, he'll want to hear all about himself!

I first became interested in horoscopes when I was working in Houston, Texas, as promotion director for a chain of department stores about to celebrate its seventh birthday. I had to find a suitable sales gimmick to get the entire state of Texas to drop everything and rush to the store.

Since seven is a mystical number, I decided to have the store's horoscope cast. A leading astrologer analyzed the store's birthday, supplying us with exciting predictions of things to come. We ran the whole report in a series of newspaper ads.

The theme was a terrific success and I've been intrigued with horoscopes ever since. In fact, I think of Korvette stores in terms of the stars. The Fifth Avenue store is a Gemini, born on May 24th and dear to me because I'm a Gemini, too. The Herald Square store, right between Macy's and Gimbel's, is a Scorpio, born November 2nd.

You may ask, "What has all this got to do with beauty?"

Anything that enriches your life, increases your intuition,

and heightens your perception must make you feel and look better. Anything that gives you a handle for dealing with other people adds to your poise. An easy lighthearted manner is attractive and appealing to those around you.

Obviously, I'm not the only one getting kicks from the stars. A leading newspaper that left out its daily horoscope one day was stormed by phone calls and personal visits from people demanding to know the predictions. A recent survey of six major cities showed that at least two-thirds of those interviewed read their daily horoscope. In Cleveland, Ohio, one hundred percent knew their birth sign!

The Fashion World loves the zodiac. Lord & Taylor, one of the most elegant stores in the world, created a Horoscope-of-Fashion concept showing in a special Stargazer's Room everything from bathing suits to evening wear. As a matter of fact, I bought a bathing ensemble in a fabric pattern bursting with all the zodiac signs.

A woman's magazine published a feature article relating food and menus to the signs of the zodiac. On television, a big special called "Signs of the Times" presented the myths and mysteries of astrology. From the recording industry Universal City Records, a division of Music Corporation of America, came out with "Discover Yourself Through Astrology," which gives a delightful analysis of all the birth signs.

When I was a student at the Nardin Academy, we studied Plato. I've forgotten most of what I studied except for one pertinent bit of advice: "Know thyself!"

Because I'm such a nut on astrology, I've got dozens of books on the subject by such authorities as Zolar, Constellation International, Carroll Righter, Constella and others. I've listened to lectures (yes, I've actually kept quiet for an hour, honest) and studied the various signs. Strictly as a nonprofessional and in an informal, friendly way, I've made a collection of beauty tendencies and characteristics of the zodiac signs.

In no way am I predicting the future. Rather, I am taking the basic characteristics of each zodiac sign as these apply to beauty. To do more than this would mean writing a whole other book.

It is in this spirit that I offer a rundown of typical tendencies as recognized by astrologers from ancient Egyptian times. Examine this information; see what it means to you.

EVE'S BEAUTY HOROSCOPE

ARIES (March 21–April 20)
You are a born leader. As the first sign of the zodiac, you possess a natural aggressiveness which is tempered by the composure of charming manners. Your body structure should allow for a basically good figure with good posture and aristocratic bearing. Your tendency to be too generous with your time and energy can cause you to skimp on the time and energy spent for your own beauty and grooming.

In fashion you have a rare intuition that stops you from wearing the "wrong" thing. You generally are neatly groomed and have a good eye for color and style. The only difficulty is the Arian tendency to be jealous. When you see someone wearing a dress or lipstick color which looks great on her, your desire to achieve the same effect may blind you to the fact that the color may not look as well on you. But don't worry. With your instincts, you can start a whole beauty trend of your own.

You are both adventurous and impatient. Your high spirits and impulsive nature can open many doors and provide many opportunities for self-expression. You have a flair for finding the out-of-the-way boutique or the warehouse of secondhand furs. Here is where you must curb your impatience and plow through the dross until you find the gold.

Those born under the sign of the Ram should relax by reading, listening to music, going to a play or concert. For extra stimulation, pick someone else's brains. Try to use your energies constructively. Your best beauty setting is the well-planned party you give in your attractive, comfortable home —with you as the beautiful hostess, running things beautifully!

ARIES BEAUTIES:	Joan Crawford	Clare Boothe Luce
	Julie Christie	Debbie Reynolds
	Mary Pickford	Doris Day
	Gloria Swanson	

TAURUS (April 21–May 20)

You are born under the rulership of Venus, the planet of love and beauty. Perhaps that is why you are so loyal and true. You are practical, strong-willed and prepared to work hard to achieve goals. This is what helps you when you decide to improve your figure through exercise and diet or to live through the trying weeks of letting your hair grow.

You are determined, stubborn. You think like a bull. You see red when somebody double-crosses you. You have the ability and forcefulness to do anything you want to do! Wherever you are, you like to run the show. Watch out for becoming officious.

Taurus women often suffer from a feeling of inferiority which results from sincere modesty. You find it hard to believe you are being appreciated and deprive yourself of the pleasure appreciation brings. Because you enjoy ritual and ceremony, you experience an almost spiritual replenishment in going to a beauty salon or taking a dance or exercise class. The routine of a shampoo, styling, manicure, and a facial do as much for the inner you as for the outer façade.

Your biggest beauty problem is a fondness for rich, spicy foods and appreciation of gourmet restaurants and good wines. You treat your family, your guests, and yourself too well at times, and must guard against weight gains and digestive upsets. Guard against neglecting the daily exercise, facial cleansing, and dental hygiene which are essential to your appearance.

Your best beauty setting is in a luscious hostess gown presiding at a magnificent table set with gleaming silver and lovely china. You are also at your best when you accept community responsibility—such as visiting hospital patients or doing volunteer work with underprivileged children. In a career, you make a terrific administrator.

TAURUS BEAUTIES: Queen Elizabeth II Shirley Temple
Margot Fonteyn Audrey Hepburn
Barbra Streisand Samantha Eggar
Candy Bergen Carol Burnett

GEMINI (May 21–June 21)
You are ruled by Mercury, the messenger of the planets. Therefore, your powers of communication are the finest of the zodiac. You should never have trouble making yourself understood. You are sophisticated, vivacious, and thrive on change. Perhaps the most sociable and outgoing of all the signs, the Gemini woman is active, adaptable, congenial, inventive. The Gemini has a driving curiosity and the charm and wit to go with it.

Manual dexterity and artistic ability show in the unique ways you wear accessories. The way you drape a scarf, place a pin or brooch, adjust a collar or belt all set you apart from the crowd.

Gemini women usually are good shoppers. Your dynamic personality and enthusiasm stirs up sales people and gets them to find exactly the blouse or gloves you want. Your love of variety means you hate to look the same twice. You love hairpieces because they enable you to change your appearance as frequently as you wish. You love new clothes and, rather than discarding old ones, you mix new with old, add accessories, and try new combinations so the total picture always seems new and different.

Your major beauty problem is controlling your impulse. Think twice before cutting off all your hair, tinting it green or buying a $5,000 sable coat on the spur of the moment.

You enjoy the challenge of change and are adaptable to any outside factors, good or bad. Your most important and fundamental need is to communicate—or die. You have a need to express your talents through acting, writing, and other forms of communication.

Your best beauty setting can be almost anywhere! Your talent for decorating can make your home or office an exciting backdrop for your "star" qualities. You need colors, shapes, and contrasts for stimulation. Avoid drab, monotonous surroundings and people since they drain your vitality, damper your spirits, and make you moody.

GEMINI BEAUTIES: Marilyn Monroe Judy Garland
                  Queen Victoria Jane Russell
                  Peggy Lee   Katherine Graham
                  Ella Fitzgerald

CANCER (June 22–July 22)

Cancer is the sign of the home and you Cancer women generally are very domestic and family-minded. Often shy and retiring, you are nevertheless capable of giving and receiving great joy and of maintaining active friendships. You are a traditionalist by nature. You save love letters forever. You collect papers, old shoes, sweaters, pocketbooks—in fact, you never throw anything out! This conservatism is also reflected in your clothes, hair, and makeup—all of which are tasteful in themselves but show your reluctance to adopt current fashions.

Cancer women are sensitive to ridicule and to criticism of personal appearance and are easily hurt. Although creative and individualistic in your ideas about life, you rarely take a chance on a hairstyle or a fashion look. Often, you may copy the style of someone you admire, a movie star or a neighbor, and hide your personality in this needless subterfuge.

Because you are perceptive and have keen powers of observation, you get good value for your shopping dollar in terms of workmanship and quality. If you can come out of your shell, you can turn these talents into vital beauty assets. As the most motherly of zodiacal signs, a Cancer woman may tend toward mothering in general. Your self-sacrificing instincts may cause you to do without the beauty aids you should have—such as skipping the professional hair-set the day your husband brings the boss home for dinner. Because of your pride in your home, you'd rather spend the time polishing the silver tea service.

Women born under this sign should guard against a sweet-tooth craving for ice cream, candy, and rich desserts. Being a good cook and homemaker, you are surrounded by delicious food and run the continuing risk of overweight. Understand, too, that you are susceptible to self-pity and sieges of despondency which affect your looks and your general health. Learn to understand these moods and find personal ways to endure them and shake them off.

Your best beauty setting is giving a children's party, a Christmas family celebration, or a reunion with old friends. In fact, anywhere where yesterday is the subject of today.

CANCER BEAUTIES: Barbara Stanwyck   Leslie Caron
                       Diahann Carroll   Kathleen Norris

LEO (July 23–August 22)
You were born to be in the limelight. You are overly generous, deeply sympathetic, and wonderfully imaginative. You are a

natural style leader, the one other women watch and imitate. Although vivacious and generous in the limelight, you must restrain any tendency to impose your views on others. Because another woman doesn't agree with your taste doesn't mean she's all wrong.

You are proud and ambitious but you must learn to control your impulses.

Leo women love luxury. You adore extravagant clothes and giving expensive gifts—and you may go into debt to get what you want. You don't feel well-dressed unless you are wearing "the best of everything." Your zest for life and your leadership skills may cause you to be involved in too many activities which overtax your strength.

Your unusually vivid imagination is expressed in your wardrobe and in your combinations of colors and fabrics. You are an innovator, the sort of woman who will start a trend— and that trend can be anything from a fad like wearing fake braids on the beach to the high fashion of white satin trenchcoats for evening.

Those born under this sign should guard against pride and flattery. Being sure of yourself may cause you to ignore advice on your appearance and warnings about your health. Your obvious need for affection may make you seem as if you're fishing for compliments and can give others the impression that you are conceited. You will never be found seeking shelter in the background and are happiest and most successful when placed in a prominent position. You must have the red-carpet treatment wherever you go—supermarket or resort—and you have such warmth that you usually get it. You can make a festive occasion out of the slightest social engagement. However, if frustrated, you can be as temperamental and rebellious as a child.

Your best beauty setting is on the stage, whether it be your living room or Radio City Music Hall. You are at your best when all eyes are on you.

LEO BEAUTIES: Princess Margaret   Jacqueline Kennedy
Connie Stevens   Shelley Winters
Hayley Mills   Lucille Ball
Mae West

VIRGO (August 22–September 22)
You are the perfectionist. You are ruled by your head rather than your emotions even though you are capable of great devotion. Practical, down-to-earth, methodical, and well-organized, you are the kind of person who never forgets to pack the right bra to wear with the dinner dress on a trip. You are always neat and attractive in appearance, though inclined to be critical of details. For you, the overall impact of an outfit is ruined if you see something wrong with one seam. When you go to a salon, it had better be spotless—or you'd rather do your beauty chores yourself!

Virgo women are rarely extravagant. You prefer to spend money on something useful and lasting rather than on frivolous or purely decorative items. Your obsession with wastefulness deprives you of passing pleasures and the sometimes surprising results of experimenting with makeup and accessories.

You are idealistic. Your standards of perfection make it impossible for you ever to be completely satisfied with the way you look—regardless of the amount of effort you put into your appearance or the degree to which your man admires the result. It's hard for you to express your true feelings so that you often are misunderstood.

As wife and mother, you guard the purse-strings and may have a tendency to nag. Your belief in the adage "a place for everything and everything in its place" can be a trial to others.

Those born under this sign have idiosyncrasies about food and frequently turn to fad diet. Because close, confining places tend to irritate you, arrange to do your work and leisure activities in as wide-open spaces as possible.

Your best beauty setting is a formal garden with perfectly manicured hedges and gorgeously trimmed rose bushes and flower beds.

VIRGO BEAUTIES:	Sophia Loren	Greta Garbo
	Grandma Moses	Lauren Bacall
	Anne Bancroft	Martha Raye

LIBRA (September 23–October 22)
You are a child of idealism. If, so far, you haven't been disenchanted by a dream or disappointment, then your outstanding charm and graciousness are at large. You have a fastidious interest in art and beauty and give meticulous attention to your appearance. You have an eye for details and proper fit plus a flair for harmony that goes beyond your wardrobe and embraces your family and friends. Because you are a romantic by nature, you find inspiration in heroines of fiction or

movies and are among the first to adopt such trademarks as the crushed beret from *Bonnie and Clyde* or the Garbo hat. You reach just decisions based on a fundamental philosophy of playing fair. You are very artistic with deep understanding. If someone believes in you, you are capable of anything.

Libra women generally abhor such menial tasks as washing a hairbrush or fixing a hem. Since your pride won't let you use the dirty hairbrush or wear anything the wrong length, you are in a constant state of frustration and your appearance may suffer. Because you are easygoing and see "both sides of a question," you may get talked into buying or doing something against your normal inclination—and then you feel guilty about backing down on your word.

You are sentimental to the extent that when a man says he likes you in a certain dress, you remember and wear it for him. Sometimes you discourage too easily, as in learning to apply eye makeup or use new grooming aides. A little perseverance will work wonders.

Those born under this sign display a surface calm but are prone to emotional upsets. Your best beauty setting is a romantic one in which there are lots of well-dressed "beautiful people"—such as at a gala concert or art gallery opening. There you can give support to the ideals of an unknown artist in whom you believe and whose dream you wish to see come true.

LIBRA BEAUTIES: Julie Andrews   Brigitte Bardot
                 Helen Hayes   Sarah Bernhardt
                 Melina Mercouri

SCORPIO (October 23–November 22)

You are dynamic, magnetic, and attractive with a talent for soothing troubled waters. However, when *you* get angry, everyone head for the hills! You function with calm efficiency in emergencies and can cope with anything from a broken leg to a fallen hem. You have a passionate nature and are radiantly beautiful when you are in love. You are very honest, treasure your possessions, and instinctively pick and run with the winners in fashion and beauty.

Scorpio women generally are good organizers and leaders. You will protect with zest everyone within your circle of life. Because of your tenacity and deep powers of concentration, you have the ability to create any beauty image you desire. Your persistence and your analytical approach to problems give you the necessary drive for making your own clothes if you don't find just what you want in the stores. These qualities also help you to master any other skills needed to achieve your beauty goals. If you can't afford them, you'll copy them.

Those born under this sign are naturally secretive and should guard against hiding health problems from themselves. Bland rather than highly spiced foods are recommended in order to avoid health disorders. When you don't win your point and become emotionally upset, you may indulge in biting sarcasm which not only stings the victims but leaves the ugly marks of a bad temper around your eyes, mouth, and heart.

Your best beauty setting is in the midst of a well-organized operation—whether it's masterminding keeping the family together, running a charity bazaar, or performing some duty of your career or home. You look your most beautiful when madly in love!

SCORPIO BEAUTIES: Katharine Hepburn   June Havoc
                      Vivien Leigh   Marlo Thomas
                      Mahalia Jackson   Joan Sutherland
                      Indira Gandhi

SAGITTARIUS (November 22–December 21)
The most important thing in life for Sagittarians is freedom and adventure. You are utterly versatile and inventive and can't be restricted. You want to be everywhere. You are broad-minded, tolerant, amiable, and tactful. Although quick-tempered and direct, you procrastinate until the last minute and have problems putting the final touches on an almost-completed project. This may include unfinished knitting, the half-decorated guest room, or the manicure that took three days to finish.

Sagittarius women are superb at "visualizing." You can pick up a pair of gloves at a sale or see a new lipstick shade in the drugstore and know how they will look. Because you have the gambler's instinct for taking a chance, you are often rewarded with surprisingly good results. This applies to your appearance in terms of letting the hair stylist "do what he wants" or trying on a dress in "a color you never wear." *You* reap the rewards—and smile at the setbacks—of the bold and daring.

Your usually sunny disposition gives you a natural, bubbly

beauty. What you must resist is an instinct toward reckless-ness which may cause you to lose your temper.

If the sound of music could create a beauty setting, it would be yours. On your magic carpet, listening to the sing-ing hills, you fasten your seat belt and travel through your imagination to the Maharajah's palace in India—even though you must prepare to have dinner with your husband and children before going off to a Broadway premiere. But dream-travel as you may, don't let anybody kid you—you'll be happy to get home tonight!

SAGITTARIUS BEAUTIES: Jane Fonda   Maria Callas
                         Mary Martin   Lillian Russell

CAPRICORN (December 22–January 19)
You are Florence Nightingale reincarnate. When anyone calls "Help!" you are there—but you'd better be given the credit for it! Your strong, ambitious drive makes you hard-working and reliable and gives you a sober sense of dignity.

You are willing to put considerable effort into maintaining a neat, attractive appearance and want more than anything to be a charmer. You may want very much to try a new hairstyle or makeup but find it hard to break through your feelings of reserve even though you'd be the first to recommend it to a friend. You are usually the last to adopt a new trend but once you get up the courage, you fully enjoy your "new look."

Capricorn women are proud of their self-sufficiency. You can't admit being in doubt about something—you'd rather die than ask for help. Your preconceived ideas may rob you of new experience and perhaps keep you from improving your appearance or situation. You need encouragement and affection—particularly from the man you love—in order to achieve your beauty potential. Your judgment is usually sound. Rely on it to steer you correctly.

Since you won't admit to doubt about a beauty or fashion decision, allow a friend whose taste you admire to help you. Your sense of thrift is a good thing when it leads to careful shopping and critical selection. You function extremely well when handling a budget at home or in your career. You are not as practical or efficient when you seek only short-term bargains in fashion and beauty and fail to consider long-term investments.

Those born under Capricorn should guard against being melancholy. You must call on your great storehouse of willpower and self-discipline to snap you out of it.

Your best beauty setting is doing something for someone else. This can be a public gesture or a personal favor—but it is essential that you believe ardently in the project or person.

CAPRICORN BEAUTIES: Marlene Dietrich   Joan of Arc
                             Patricia Neal   Ethel Merman

AQUARIUS (January 20–February 18)
You are the most versatile of all signs, inventive and quick. You are often individualistic and unconventional. Extremely creative, you are the kind of person who can convert the bedroom curtains into a ballgown—and then may moodily decide to stay home to read an interesting book!

Aquarius women, though temperamental, are inherently

kind. You may drive your hairdresser batty with your demands but you also remember his birthday and sense at once if he is tired or unhappy about something. Because you have an analytical mind, you can recognize and understand the nature of a fashion trend and extract the best aspects. This talent serves you well since it allows you to keep up with the latest fashions without going to extremes.

You have a great memory and a knack for learning easily. For you, a professional makeup lesson is a good investment since you will be able to repeat all the steps by yourself once you get home. Dancing, exercise classes, and other self-improvement courses also have this built-in bonus.

Your ability to take quick action serves you well at things like auctions—unless you let your emotions lead the way. In other words, if a flashy blonde in a leopard coat goes after the same Wedgwood vase you have your eye on, you'll either let her have it without a murmur or race her for it. Get it or forget it!

Your best beauty setting is in the midst of bustling activity. If twenty things are going on at once and there is lots of razzle-dazzle, such as at a Country Fair, a rodeo or circus, a race track or even a flea market with lots of stalls and people shouting, you are in your element. You look wonderful arranging flowers in a lovely bowl but you like six or seven varieties to work into a magnificent grouping. If you have only roses, you're bored by their sameness.

AQUARIUS BEAUTIES:	Zsa Zsa Gabor	Lana Turner
	Tammy Grimes	Tallulah Bankhead
	Ann Sothern	Marian Anderson
	Katharine Cornell	

PISCES (February 19–March 20)
You are continually at odds with the contradictory forces of
your nature. Come on, now, cultivate the romantic aspect of
your personality. You have the ability to be charming, magnetic, attractive, but sometimes you are overcome with shy-
ness which others may misinterpret.

You possess ingenuity, a deep sense of beauty, and a
powerful imagination. Your wonderful and sometimes zany
sense of humor shows up delightfully in your wardrobe and
home decor. Because of your fondness for indulging in romantic daydreams, you may be disappointed when others
don't respond or are unable to join in the spirit of things.
Pisceans often are very sentimental and should keep personal
mementos around them for sustenance.

You are exceptionally generous and tolerant, with a natural
gift for persuasion. The only trouble is, you sometimes get
carried away by your desire to help and when your contribu-
tion is not fully appreciated, you feel martyred. To achieve
the most gratification, use this drive to work on community
projects and with your own children.

Use this drive, also, to discover more about yourself. Find
out why the hairdo you adored last week is the one you hate
this week. You over-react to what others think about you.
Make up your own mind. If a neighbor suggests you move the
piano, is the move really what you want? If, suddenly, you
don't like your handbag, try to remember if someone disap-
proved of it.

You are highly susceptible to the ills of those you love so
guard against sympathetic aches and pains. When someone
is sick, you're great at engaging the best doctors, and sending

flowers and get-well notes. But you have a bad bedside manner! You are impatient with illness because you can't do anything about it. You are sensitive to pain and suffering and find it difficult to hide these feelings from the patient—so you run.

Your best beauty setting is among classical music, beautiful paintings, and rich fabrics. They contribute much to your feelings of contentment and your personal appearance responds accordingly. Instinctively, you choose the best of everything, whether colors and textures for your home or fashions and cosmetics that highlight your best features.

PISCES BEAUTIES: Elizabeth Taylor   Patty Duke
Mia Farrow   Ursula Andress
Liza Minelli   Dinah Shore

Right in the Palm of Your Hand

If I hear anyone complain, "She talks with her hands," I go out of my mind! I remember that after being on Virginia Graham's TV show one time, I asked Warren how I made out. He said, "Next time, I supply the handcuffs."

Think how much people say with their hands, waving them around, punching the air for emphasis, and imagine what one can tell by looking into their palms!

Hands are a part of you and tell a lot about you. The left hand is connected to the right side of your brain, the right hand is connected to the left. What is so startling is that once you can identify some of the basic lines, a person's palm may indicate an entirely different person from the one whose hand you hold and whom you think you know. Even more startling, when you read the palm lines aloud, your subject will probably look at you in amazement and say, "You're absolutely right!"

Okay, so you're at a party and you have to make conversation with this person you've never met before. You've already exhausted all conversation about his horoscope. What next? You can have him eating out of the palm of your hand by reading *his*. First, find out if he's right- or left-handed by simply watching which he uses most—or just ask him!

Since this section on palmistry is for fun at parties and not meant as a textbook or training course, I'm only going to tell you about the three basic hand shapes with the three basic (and easiest to see) palm lines. There are actually seven shapes but assuming you're not going to go professional, three's enough for fun. If you get really interested in the science, there are plenty of books on the subject.

The first—and I think best—book I ever read on palmistry is called *Palmistry for All* by Cherio, published in 1916 and now out of print. Cherio teaches that for a right-handed person the left hand shows inherited tendencies, and the right hand shows the developed or cultivated qualities. For left-handed people, the theory is reversed.

On a long train or plane ride or at a party you can always stir things up by peering into a nearby palm. Of course, there's always someone who will say, "I'm ambidextrous!" From the palmistry point of view, nobody can be ambidextrous unless the lines on both palms are almost identical!

Three Basic Hand Shapes

The seven fundamental shapes range from the very earthy to the extremely idealistic, but most hands fall into three general categories that are easy for the amateur like you and me to recognize during a social situation—while the hostess is pouring the tea or you're making small talk with your dancing partner.

The short, square, squat, strong hand: Here is an earthy, no-nonsense type. If your man has this shape hand, he is a useful, contributing person, one you can really count on. If this describes your own hand, you're wonderful in the kitchen, very adept with your hands, responsible, and rarely take anything for granted. You're the kind of person who wants proof. If someone said to you, "There's a new sable coat in that closet," you wouldn't take his word for it. You'd have to open the door to see for yourself.

The graceful, tapering, pointed hand: Here is a philosophical and often artistic type. This shape indicates an artistic temperament and optimistic, high ideals, the degree to which the individual is artistic or idealistic depending on the Head Line. A man with this kind of hand likes a spiritual woman and would be offended by one who tells an off-color joke. He wants his goddess on a pedestal. If this is your shape hand, you tend to believe in everybody and everything. People have to really "do you wrong" before you will think ill of them. You are the kind of woman who could sit on the piano and sing, "He's Just My Bill" and break every heart with your feeling and sincerity.

The very long, lean, tapered hand: The hand that is extremely long between the wrist and the fingers, with a long, slim thumb and little finger, indicates a person with a very high intelligence level and unusual gifts of intuition. This is the kind of person you can call and say, "Guess who?"—and he'll hit it right on the head! This type is often very impractical. If it's you, you'd better have a maid, butler, gardener, and personal secretary to attend to the details of everyday life. If a man has this shape hand he'd better be loaded and I mean with hard cash, not hard liquor, because he's useless at business and is best suited for the highest forms of the arts— painting, music, and writing—and too often, these don't buy the groceries!

Three Basic Palm Lines

The Life Line: It starts between the index finger and thumb and moves downward across the palm. A long Life Line means chances are good that you will live a long time, so

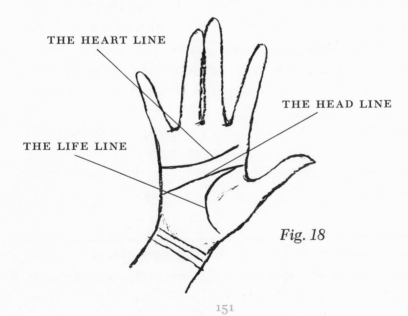

THE HEART LINE

THE HEAD LINE

THE LIFE LINE

Fig. 18

start counting on Medicare right now. But don't be fooled by a shorter Life Line—what's important is how deep and how wide the line is.

A broad Life Line, for instance, indicates a robust constitution. It may be shorter but, because of its strength, it conquers all problems.

If the Life Line starts out joined to the Head Line (as shown in illustration), the person is well-balanced. If the Life Line starts out *above* the Head Line, this is a sign of great dependence. If there's a distance between the Life Line and the Head Line, there is great independence.

Most people have a space between the two lines. Everyone loves to be independent, so when you see this space, you can rightly say, "Boy, are you independent!" You've intrigued your audience right there!

The Head Line: Probably the most important single line in the palm, it indicates the degree of mentality. In the illustration, you see an average Head Line. If you're gazing at a palm in which the Head Line slant dips a lot lower than that in the illustration, the person is extremely idealistic. If the Head Line goes straight across the palm, he's more practical. If it forks upward, he's very materialistic.

For party patter, you can interpret these differences by saying, "Ah, you have a sound, practical nature. You're the kind of person who adds up the bill in the restaurant."

Or, for the materialistic person, "You take great pleasure in your possessions. Only the best is good enough for you."

The Heart (Love) Line: This line tells you about someone's affectionate and emotional nature. As you can see in the illustration, the Heart Line begins at the outside edge of the hand and generally ends up under the index finger. Shown is the normal Heart Line. Sometimes it may curve up between the index and middle finger or zoom over beyond the end of the index finger.

When the Heart Line is extremely long, the tendency is to be very jealous. If the palm belongs to a man you've just met, here's a tip—if you get him, he'll take care of you forever! But he is possessive, so if you so much as look at anybody else, you're in trouble.

When the Heart Line resembles the illustration, the person is affectionate and giving, the kind who makes the world happy and well, someone wonderful who is firm and reliable in love and has a high code of honor and morals.

The Heart Line that shoots high up under the index finger means this is someone special. When he loves, he loves forever! Chances are, he doesn't believe in second marriages or playing the field.

If the Heart Line is closer to the Head Line than in the illustration, here is a person who is always torn between romantic fancy and the practical aspects of life, a constant struggle between heart and head.

The most important thing to remember is that each line must be related to the whole picture. If the Head Line is practical and the Heart Line is full of love for the entire world, isn't that a lovely combination?

In Job 37:7 we find these significant words: "God caused the signs or seals on the hands of all the sons of men, that the sons of men might know their works."

I certainly don't advise hanging out a shingle, "Palms read here," but I do feel palmistry is a great conversation piece at parties and to amuse your husband's friends and enjoy all the "secrets" you uncover.

Take it from Eve:
P.S. If you read your own palm and don't like it, just remember to keep your hands under the table or to wear gloves!

P.P.S. I haven't gone into the subject of "mounds," the fleshy parts of the hands because it would get too complicated for this little summary, but I will tell you this: The mound of flesh directly under the thumb is called the Mound of Venus. It's size indicates how sexy you are—the bigger the better!

The Handwriting Is on the Wall

The more you know about handwriting, the better you will be able to understand the person who does the writing.

There's no mumbo jumbo about handwriting analysis. You may learn enough about it to put on a turban and set up a booth at a local charity bazaar. But you don't need Madame Arkady's "special powers" or extrasensory perception. In fact, the only sense you really need is the common sense to follow a few basic rules that are, for the most part, so obvious you'll wonder why you didn't think of them yourself.

A good example might be the informal note you get from a dear friend inviting you to have lunch with her. You haven't seen each other in weeks and it will be fun to get together. Then you wonder, "Is anything wrong? Does she have good news or bad?" You read her note again.

Her handwriting will give you a clue as to what you can

expect. It will certainly tell you how she felt when she wrote the note. If her handwriting ran downhill across the page, she was feeling pessimistic, so plan to give her a sympathetic ear over the tomato surprise.

On the other hand—no pun intended—if her words travel uphill, forget your diet and plan to spend a delightful three hours over lunch instead of the usual two. She's in great, optimistic spirits, and you're going to have a high old time.

Remember "Mirror, Mirror, on the wall . . . ," and how the mirror tells no lies? The same thing is true about handwriting. Whether you know what each little squiggle signifies or not, you probably get an instinctive "message" from what you see. Isn't it true that sometimes you get a letter and something tells you what's inside before you even open it?

You can turn these intuitive hunches into meaningful analysis. If you're as intrigued with the complexity of the human animal as I am, you'll love having a rudimentary knowledge of handwriting. With it, you can entertain guests at parties, liven up a cruise, and learn a little bit more about your friends and associates.

Best of all, you can take a dispassionate look at your own handwriting and find out some things about yourself. Handwriting reveals mood as well as character. For instance, take a piece of paper and write a few lines to someone you love.

"I love you, George!"

Then, take a fresh sheet of paper and write a hypothetical note to the credit manager of a department store that has been hounding you for an unpaid bill which you have paid. *Grrrrrrr*. "Dear Mr. Birch: There seems to be an error in your records. . . ."

Finally, scribble a quick note of instructions to your child or the baby-sitter. "Please remember to close all the windows before you go out. . . ."

Of course, it's a better test if you happen to have some notes of this kind hanging around—maybe the postcard you sent your husband from the Chinese restaurant, and so on. Whichever the case, put all your own handwriting samples together before you and you will instantly see the differences between the way you write as a loving wife, an angry customer, and an efficient mother.

Yet however different the various forms of your handwriting may seem, there are basic things that don't change. That is why banks can spot a forgery. Your signature will look different at different times depending on the circumstances at the time of signing. Obviously, if you're harassed by fifty people standing behind you at the airlines ticket counter, your signature will not look much like that written in the privacy of your own house. But the basics of your signature are constant. The authenticity is there.

How does all this relate to your beauty? Handwriting analysis is an extension of knowledge and intuition. The more you know about people, the more beautiful you become. If you can entertain guests at a party, put people at ease by recognizing their insecurities, they will respond to you with affection and admiration.

It would be silly to pretend that a scrap of paper is going to reveal the whole secret life of a person you meet at a clambake, but the following basic rules will tip you off to the broad indications of character traits, social attitudes, and emotional hang-ups.

Personality has many channels of expressions—one of them

being through the tip of your ballpoint pen. All you need is some unlined paper and a pen. The writing should be spontaneous so don't let your subject copy a passage from a book. Be sure you get a signature, too, since this is often very different in style from the rest of the handwriting.

If you want to be fancy, use a magnifying glass for close examination of dotted "i's"—but it's certainly not necessary.

Now, smile mysteriously . . . and consider the following:

Slant: This is a sign of affection. Everyone is affectionate but the problem is the ability to express it. That's where the slant comes in. If the letters lean forward slightly, the person has an easy, affectionate nature and is someone who gets along well with people and loves to socialize. If the handwriting slants very far forward, however, this means an over-eagerness to please and the subject may be too possessive at times. This sort of person tends to have unhappy love affairs, expecting too much too soon.

Conversely, a slightly backward slant means the head controls the heart. This does not mean a lack of capacity for love, but only that the person is slower to show emotion and enthusiasm.

An extremely backward slant suggests that an aloof, cold exterior is hiding a volcano of emotional fire inside! Wow! (Unless the person happens to be left-handed.)

If the letters are up-and-down vertical, your subject is a calm, harmonious individual who accepts life as it comes with equanimity.

Often, the slant of handwriting will change several times in a letter. This shows that the intellect and the emotions are fighting it out. The mind wants one thing, the heart another.

Such people are usually fascinating to be with because you never know what to expect!

Uphill or Downhill: The reason for testing on unlined paper is to see whether the inclination is to write up the paper, down, or to take off in several directions at once. Draw straight lines under each handwritten line to clearly see the direction.

As I pointed out earlier in discussing what a lunch invitation might really be saying, writing that runs slightly uphill shows optimism, confidence, and a generally cheery outlook. Extreme uphill writing may show that the writer's head is in the clouds with a tendency to disregard reality.

Rapidly descending lines mean you are dealing with a gloomy, pessimistic soul (let's hope it's temporary). A mildly downhill tendency probably means a healthy caution and slight skepticism.

If the message slips up and down like a roller coaster, you're talking to someone who is indecisive, moody, and has trouble adjusting to routine. Since this is a pretty harsh thing to say to anyone at a party and since we're just amateurs, the best way to analyze up-and-down writing is to point out that the person is impatient with dull routine and hates details.

Spacing: Does this dreamy man you're analyzing spend his money or hang onto it for dear life? Is he a generous host, a thoughtful friend, a considerate employer? Ah-ha! You can tell by the spaces between the words. Wide spaces between words and between lines show generosity. Did I hear you say, "Elementary, dear Watson!"? You're getting the idea. But don't get carried away. If the spaces are disproportionately wide, that means the money slips through his fingers like sand and that he is given to wildly extravagant gestures.

It would seem logical that words crammed closely together would indicate thriftiness or, in the extreme, miserliness. But don't confuse the space between words with the size of words. A person who writes big letters nevertheless may leave no space between words. If that's so, watch and see if he's the one who fumbles for the check.

Margins: Margins are a good indication of giving. Wide margins disclose good taste and pleasure in the delights of life. If there's a wide margin on the left and right but no space top and bottom, you can expect that natural generosity is hampered by poor judgment.

If there's a wide margin on the left side only, with a narrow right margin, the subject is probably extravagant by instinct but tries to overcome it with pointless penny-wise savings— like sending a postcard instead of phoning.

The Dot: There are many ways to dot an "i." To figure out what the dot means, you must judge it in the context of the rest of the writing. For instance, if you see light, easygoing penmanship with a heavy dot, the person is most likely forceful and opinionated. A circle dot indicates a creative person who is looking for a means of expression and wants to be noticed, the kind of person who changes her name from Jane to Jayne.

Here's where your magnifying glass can be useful. You can tell a lot about the subject's sense of humor by the dot. A half-circle, crescent, wavy line, or any kind of blob reveals a good sense of humor. In fact, the zanier the dot, the wittier and more delightful the personality.

If the writing is heavy, a light, precise dot shows a deliberate, serious view of life. A blunt dot that points downward means watch out for stubborn opinions. Dots that are sprinkled all over the place like freckles or that turn into dashes are signs of a lively imagination and a seeker of new ideas.

Legibility: Here there are so many variables, you won't be able to make any snap judgments. However, there's plenty you can talk about and that's what makes handwriting analysis such fun.

For instance, orderly well-formed letters and crystal-clear writing may reveal an ability to think clearly and a desire to communicate with others. This writing shows intelligence but its very clarity may indicate a lack of creativity.

At the other extreme, handwriting that zooms across the page like galloping ski tracks may seem illegible but speed is usually the result of a quick mind. The hand can't keep up with the tumbling thoughts. Yet, if you look closely, you will be surprised to see that this seemingly chaotic handwriting is actually easy to read.

Between the two extremes, there's clear writing with distinctive formations that set it apart from copybook penmanship. If the capital letters are absolutely simple, with no flourishes or curlicues, the person is strong, capable, and receptive to change and new ideas.

When words are unreadable, disorderly, and all mushed together, these are signs of impatience, suspicion, and moodiness. This person may be difficult to understand and is consequently unhappy and at odds with the world.

One thing you should be sure to do in any of these analyses is to consider the profession or background of the subject. Teachers, accountants, librarians, and others with specialized lives have trained themselves to write carefully and clearly for their work. The housewife who writes very little, the businessman who dictates correspondence, or the student who types most things at first may seem inhibited and strained in their handwriting. If this seems the case, ask them to do another sample after they've had a chance to relax.

With a basic knowledge and a lively interest in horoscopes, palmistry, and handwriting, you can take a leaf from the great Irish poet-philosopher, James Stephens, who wrote in *The Crock of Gold:* "Women are wiser than men because they know less and understand more." Try it!

Take It from Eve

Someone once said about me, "Eve is the only person I know who was born with a silver spoon in her mouth and turned it into solid gold."

This was a flowery compliment and it made me realize two things. I was lucky to be born into a large, loving and financially comfortable family. Nourished by the security and affection of my youth, I was able to go out and compete in the business world for the sheer fun and exhilaration of it all —and not to compensate for early deprivation.

I was born the last of seventeen children on my father's fiftieth birthday in Buffalo, New York, and grew up the "spoiled brat" in an eight-bedroom Italian household—pampered and petted by many sisters and brothers. By the time I came along, my brothers were grown up and successful, things were financially good, and the atmosphere was warm with love.

Spoiled I may have been. I had a mink coat at sixteen, a diamond bracelet the next year, and for my high school graduation, a shiny convertible was outside the door with my beaming brothers waiting to see me get behind the wheel. Yet, I don't feel spoiled. Being given wonderful things showed me the meaning of generosity and how nice it is to give as well as get. I can't believe a family's love and attention ever really spoil a child. After all, if nobody ever gives you anything, you have nothing to give back.

Through these growing-up years and since, I've been grateful for my family and I have never forgotten my mother's words, "Whatever you do, whatever you say, it's got to come from your heart!"

I think of her words every day. I have tried to live from the heart and also to get right to the heart of the problems and situations that comprise our lives. To me, living from the heart is a clarion call for personal style and individual conviction and it sums up the philosophy we are discussing in this book.

Getting directly to the heart of things means cut out the nonsense, don't take detours, avoid being bogged down by foolish obstacles, and accentuate the positive.

TRAVEL

Take that old troublemaker Travel, for instance.

Okay, let's *take* travel. Or, rather, let's take your next vacation trip. It's going to be a dilly. You've been flipping through travel folders for weeks. You've made all the arrangements. You've promised yourself this trip will make personal travel history for you, transforming you into a new person, relieving you of all your fatigue, anxiety and dullness. So, what's the first thing you do?

You make a vow to travel light. Right? WRONG!

To my mind, the only way to travel is to travel *heavy!* Now, I'm not talking about a quick business trip to St. Louis or a weekend jaunt with the in-laws in Texas. What I am getting all emotional about is the compulsion of so many women to go away on a luxurious vacation trip to Europe or the Far East or to some of the livelier American resorts with a skimpy wardrobe—and why? To stay within the weight limits set by the airlines.

My feeling is, if you don't travel with the right clothes and accessories, you might as well stay home! I've seen American women traveling in Europe with their husbands and looking like prison guards in drab drip-dries and all-black accessories because they "go with everything." These women wouldn't be caught dead in these dreary things at home or at the country club. But here they are, at a Paris nightclub, in a "nothing" dress wearing "nothing" shoes, their hair a mess because they arrived in Paris too late to get their hair done and, of course, they left their wigs back home in Scarsdale or Chevy Case because why?

"Because I didn't want to be overweight on the plane!"

For the married woman, vacation travel is a rare opportunity to be alone with her husband away from home. It can be another honeymoon or it can be a bomb. For this reason alone, it's essential to pack everything you need to look and feel your loveliest en route to your destinations, in hotel rooms, aboard excursion ships, trains, and the like.

Travel can be very romantic and it is up to the wife to maintain the romantic aura. A few years ago, my husband suddenly announced it was spring and that we should go to Paris for a long weekend. It was a spur-of-the-moment impulse. He had no business reason to go. We would simply check in at the Ritz if only for four days.

Four days or not, you can believe me I didn't travel light on that trip! The essence of romance is always there. Just don't ignore it or throw it away.

Take the negligee. It may seem practical to wear your raincoat as a bathrobe but think how it will look having your coffee on the tiny balcony overlooking the Champs Elysées?

Take more than enough shoes. Not only will you be more

comfortable but you will be set to meet any shoe emergency. It's a peculiar thing about travel but shoes that can take anything around home base have a tendency to go all weak and snap heels or pop their trimmings at exactly the wrong moment when you're away.

Take your wig-case with your wig or fall freshly cleaned and set, plus a hair accessory or two to "save your life." A vacation is supposed to be fun. How much fun can it be if your hair looks like a mildewed poodle?

Take all essential beauty preparations and accessories—and I mean *all.* It's amazing how many efficient women will go away for three weeks and decide not to take essentials like hair-spray or bath powder or eye makeup remover pads which they use every single solitary day at home *because they take up too much room.*

Take it from Eve:

1. You go on vacation to have a good time. You can't have a good time unless you look well. You can't look well unless you have a well-rounded wardrobe and the right accessories and grooming aids.

2. If you're on a tight budget, spend less on fares and hotels in order to cover your beauty and fashion needs. They are needs, not frivolity. In other words, if you haven't saved enough out of your household allowance to cover overweight, stay one day less and really enjoy it instead of being secretly miserable, saying to yourself, "If I only had my red crepe. If I had only taken the silver shoes."

3. Don't begrudge the cost of overweight. Consider it a

legitimate travel expense like anything else. It hurts less that way.

4. In the bustle of packing, your husband may say, "Don't take that. We can always buy it there." Smile a lot and pack it anyhow. It's possible you can buy it there—if only the shops aren't closed because of a national holiday or they just ran out.

And if he complains about taking too much, use this story as your guide. On a vacation at Dorado Beach, Puerto Rico, Warren and I spent part of each day lounging around at poolside. Our very first morning, we noticed an extremely attractive woman wearing a spectacular striped bathing suit, the kind you notice and remember. The next day, she wore it again. For seven straight days, she appeared in the exact same suit—unless she had several copies of the same design.

By week's end, Warren's fascination with her had turned into mild exasperation. "Why can't she wear something different?" he wanted to know. When you're at a resort, you owe it to yourself and the other guests to be a decorative part of the scenery.

See! Husbands are funny! They are also very proud. They want their wives to look wonderful and be a source of admiration. They may not often admit it but their wives' travel wardrobes are something they enjoy talking about.

In fact, my husband often complains with pride, "My wife travels for three days as if it were three years."

PARTIES

Another area where I relate back to my mother's words about the need to put your heart into things is in party-giving and entertaining others. It's true there aren't very many really bad parties anymore. Most people have acquired the knack of removing ice cubes from ice trays without dropping them on the floor. The trouble is, there are not enough really great parties.

Okay, so you cooked up a giant tub of Bulgarian goulash. You've drugged the children and tied them into bed. You've spent hours polishing the silver. You've cracked a nail opening the Macadamian nuts. You've got enough liquid refreshment to float the Elizabeth II and you think that about does it.

To me, the usual party formula of food, booze, the men over there, and the women over here is strictly for the birds. A good party is like a theatrical production. It must be planned down to the smallest detail and right up to the last exit cue.

Too often, I get the feeling that the main reason for a party is to pay back social obligations or start some. True as this may be, the primary purpose of a party should be to see that people have a good time.

To put it mildly, I adore parties. I love giving them; I love going to them. After years of doing both, I would say the most important ingredient for a successful party is to individualize each guest. If you can make everyone feel personally cherished and not just part of the furniture, you've got a great party going. It doesn't matter if you spend ten dollars or ten times that on refreshments and decor.

Some of the most entertaining evenings my husband and I ever spend are at dinner parties given by our friends, the Solons, who own the famous Meredith Galleries in New York. Our host and hostess take the trouble to prepare individual toasts for each guest. When we sit down to dinner, they give the toasts to each of us in turn, the host honoring the ladies, the hostess the men. Each of us has a moment of glory, a chance to shine alone in the spotlight of everyone's attention.

It's fabulous! All the toasts are flattering, of course—that's what parties are for, to make everyone feel good, and to mention a personal triumph or idiosyncrasy of the one being toasted. Conversation could be a little sluggish before dinner. Now the toasts relax inhibitions and the atmosphere at the dinner table becomes so electrified with pleasure that even, "Please pass the salt," is suddenly a hilariously funny remark.

It is the feeling of good spirits at a party that counts more than what's said. One year, Warren and I were in Rome to confer with Aldo Via Condotte, one of the foremost Italian hair stylists. After so much emphasis on English hairdressing, I thought it would be fun to invite Signor Aldo on a tour of the Eve Nelson salons and bring a new, fresh influence to American women.

To celebrate our new friendship, we gave a party for Aldo at our Hotel Excelsior suite, and as the guests poured in we realized that most of them spoke no English. We speak practically no Italian, but it didn't matter. We all had a great time. It wasn't what we said to each other but our willingness to communicate hospitality and mutual good fellowship.

Another time, back home in New York, Warren and I decided it was time to give a humdinger of a party. I'm crazy about horoscopes so we had personalized horoscopes prepared for all the guest's birth signs. Each analysis was read aloud with such descriptions of character as "warm, sensitive, and deeply creative but tends to be frivolous." It was a mild sensation with everyone laughing and joking freely—knowing their turn would come soon enough.

The horoscope theme has become so popular, I have built up a collection of zodiac ashtrays, lighters, and coasters so each person can have his own sign. For personalized gifts, too, I think the recipient's birth sign is a more original touch than initials or a monogram.

Warren and I once gave a party for a number of his business associates. Some gimmick was needed to break the ice as most of the guests had never met before. I love handwriting analysis, so what did we do? We brought in a handwriting expert and asked all the guests to jot down an unsigned message on a piece of paper. After the party had been simmering along for about an hour, the guests assembled and the expert analyzed each piece of paper, describing the person who wrote the message and predicting something wonderful and exciting for the future. The gimmick worked and I learned a lot about handwriting that night, enough to interest me in studying the subject further.

Party Games

Some people sneer about party games; don't sneer around me. When you talk about party games around me, pardner, SMILE. I love them. I've found, too, that in my world of fashion and beauty and in my husband's world of the oil business, the busiest and most successful people are the ones who love games most.

Now do you love games?

One that breaks me up and always builds up party excitement is "In the Manner of the Word." I learned it from Mrs. Schmeck, wife of the publisher of *The Baltimore Sun,* who invited a group of us to their suite at the Waldorf Astoria in New York after a newspaper publishers' dinner and said, "Do you like games?"

"In the Manner of the Word" is a mild form of charades and you don't have to know what Hamlet whispered under his breath to Ophelia in order to play it. The rules are simple. One person goes out of the room. Those remaining agree on a single word (not a phrase) which must be an adverb or an adjective.

The one who returns must guess the word by asking each person in turn to do something "in the manner of the word." For instance, "Dance with me in the manner of the word." If the word were *angrily,* the dance would be a snarling, grimacing, glaring turn around the floor. If the word were *rapid* and the person was asked, "Smoke in the manner of the word," he could wind up with an imitation of Bette Davis puffing a cigarette as if it were going out of style.

Party Themes

A party theme is like a musical cue in a movie. It puts you in a certain mood and tells you what to expect. As a hostess, you are like a movie director. It's up to you to set the scene, get the action going, and cue your guests on their roles in the production.

In our many years of entertaining leaders in industry, fashion, and finance, I've learned one basic truth. Successful people adore parties with themes. They love the chance to let their hair down and have fun. They want to forget about work, responsibilities, and the millions of problems awaiting their attention the next day. What they don't want is to stand around, fruitlessly making party talk about "How do you think the market's going to go?"

Don't be intimidated by the party themes you read about in the papers or *Life* magazine. Because Truman Capote gave a masked ball in New York and Count Whoosis-Whatsis threw a little Italian barbecue on the canals in Venice, you may feel you need a *palazzo* or at least a thirty-room shack in order to give a unique party.

Right?

Wrong, again! All you need to create a theme is imagination and careful planning. Also, it's not against the rules to take the idea of a jazzy jet-set party and scale it down to size.

A few years ago, I remember, Broadway producer David Merrick gave a party for the opening night of *The World of Susie Wong*. Not a man to do things inconspicuously, he took over New York's entire Chinatown section for the evening. There was music and singing in the streets, giant placards welcoming everyone in behalf of Suzie Wong. Jugglers, dancers, and magicians performed. Each guest received a package of Suzie Wong paper money to "spend" for food, drink and souvenirs.

It was a real grabber. The most jaded, worldly of first-nighters had the times of their lives, spending their paper money, arguing jovially with each other about whether they could afford two egg rolls or whether they should save their money for a paper fan, a pot of tea or an incense burner.

A magical, nonsensical atmosphere had been created and the guests entered into the spirit of things with delight. But —paper money is cheap, especially if you liberate some from your kids. For your next backyard buffet, why not "sell" the food for paper money and maybe wrap up a lot of prizes with varying price tags on them as souvenirs. I have found that the best prizes are dime store items that give guests a nostalgic kick, like a Yo-Yo, jacks, jump-rope, bat-ball, spinning top, puzzles. The actual food theme here could vary from a Western cookout to an Italian festival or right back with Suzie Wong and an exotic Oriental bazaar.

Easter Sunday is a big event for Warren and me. We take special pleasure in celebrating and usually have a brunch. Last year, we had an Easter Egg Hunt—not in our seventy-five-room mansion because we don't have a seventy-five-room mansion (that man is so mean to me!) but right in our five-room Manhattan apartment. This may seem too small for an egg hunt but it works and it's fun!

We had as much fun before everyone arrived as after. I had gathered eggs in four sizes, regular hard-boiled hen eggs plus foil-covered chocolate eggs in three smaller sizes. You got points for the eggs found, less for the larger ones since they were easier to spot.

Each guest was given a hug, a drink, and a plastic bag for the eggs. It was hilarious with everyone crawling around the furniture, digging under cushions, peeking behind pictures. There were crazy prizes for everyone, naturally. Grown-ups like prizes as much as children.

I had asked an artist friend, Joe Attone, to sketch some

quick portraits of the other guests on hard-boiled eggs which each received when it came time to eat. Can you believe it—one guest, a fashion expert, won all the prizes!

Another time, for a dear friend's birthday, I brooded and brooded, trying to think up a good party idea. Then, it hit me! All of our mutual friends had varying ethnic backgrounds. It would be a kind of United Nations dinner. All the guests were asked to bring one cooked dish from their country of origin, however many generations back that might be.

The table was a symphony (if I must say so myself) of silver, china, flowers and candelabra. I had found tiny flags of all nations and assembled them as a centerpiece. Warren cooked up his masterpiece: Swedish meat balls. I remembered all my momma had ever taught me for a rich, Italian spaghetti. Friends brought Hungarian goulash, Sauerbraten, steak and kidney pie, Greek salad, among others.

We all had a small portion of everything and, as the evening wore on, we reminisced about the diversity of our childhood memories and marveled at the wonder of living in the United States where people with such contrasting backgrounds can live together.

Tape recorders and cameras are a party-giver's friends. Sometimes, they enable you to pull a fast one on friends (and I don't mean by putting a tape recorder in unmentionable places!). Last year, when Warren and I got back from a vacation trip, we invited a group of friends over. When they got there, we announced, "Guess what! We're going to show you our travel films. Isn't that great?"

The enthusiasm was such that I could hear happy little

cries of, "Let's get the hell out of here!" and "I told you I was too tired to go out!"

Undaunted, we set up the screen and the projector. Warren turned off the lights. The film began. What do you suppose we showed?

Not Paris in the spring.

Not San Francisco at dawn.

Not an out-of-focus volcano or me patting a donkey or vice-versa.

As our disgruntled guests soon discovered, the film was of them! For months, Warren and I had been collecting footage taken at football games, parties, summer weekends and so on. We had edited the film and written a commentary to go with it.

Surprises are always great and this was one greater yet because it was mixed with the relief of not having to sit through four hours of The Nelsons on Vacation. They giggled. They howled. We punched each other—"There I am!" . . . "Oh, I look awful. I'll sue you!" . . . "Remember that? Grounds for divorce!"

This idea of surprising guests with pictures of themselves reminds me of a Long Island hostess who makes personalized place cards for each guest by using the person's photograph instead of his name.

In a way, giving a good party got me my wonderful husband. We probably would have married anyway, but a few months after we met, his birthday rolled around and I gave him a "This Is Your Life" party. Using the format of the then-famous television show, he had to sit on a couch while from behind a curtain, friends and business associates told an anecdote or reminisced about their past. They loved it. Warren loved it. The next year, we were married. That was in 1953 and we haven't had a dull moment since!

(Warren, if you're reading this part—I love you!)

Take it from Eve:

There's no such thing as an unplanned party. Studied casualness can only come from precise attention to details and genuine caring about guests' pleasure and comfort.

Take it from Eve:

When it comes to refreshments, offer a variety of tastes and textures. You can't please everyone—but you can have *something* that will please everyone. Instead of cooking up two barrels of one thing, make half-barrels of several things. If you prepare hot, spicy dishes, however delicious and sensational, have a benevolent thought for the guest who doesn't or shouldn't like having his throat scorched. A bland casserole or platter of meats and cheese are good contrast to "hot" dishes and may be the entire meal for some guests.

Two of My Favorite Party Menus

Here are two basic menus I use, with variations. One is for a buffet, the other, a sit-down dinner.

EVE NELSON BUFFET

My Own Tossed Green Salad
four kinds of lettuce, chilled crisp, tomatoes, radishes and just
enough watercress to show. Plus sweet red onions cut in rings so
non-onion people can avoid them.

Toasted Thin Rye & Corn Muffins

Lobster Newburgh
(Don't be stingy with the lobster!)

Champagne-glazed Baked Ham
(the kind with cloves and crushed pineapple)

Fluffy Rice
with chopped chives, parsley and butter, delicious alone or with
the lobster or ham.

Fresh Fruit Boat
a mountain of fresh fruit salad in the shell of a watermelon, honey-
dew or pineapple, depending on season.

EVE NELSON SIT-DOWN DINNER

Turtle Soup
with wine, of course

Baked Pastry Shell with Fish
either crabmeat or lobster with a lovely sauce, baked and served
in a beautiful shell—with a little pimento for color

Special Beef Filet
nothing is more elegant

Tiny Roast Potatoes
or sweet potatoes in season

Two In-season Vegetables
try stringbeans in tomato sauce with grated cheese and chopped almonds on top

Individual Ice Cream Molds
the shapes appropriate to the party—or in zodiac signs

Petits Fours

About Wines

For buffet or sit-down meals, wines add gourmet enjoyment to good food and good company. I don't believe in the old rules about red wine with meats and white wine with poultry and fish. Have both and let your guests follow their own preference. A sweet wine may be served with dessert, liqueurs with or after the coffee.

Take it from Eve:

Many a hostess allows only a half hour for cocktails before dinner. While I don't think guests should be given too much to drink before the meal is served, a half hour is too short a time for people to unwind and get acquainted. To me, an hour works very well to get the party moving and I always serve tasty little hot hors d'oeuvres to kill the hunger pangs of those who are starved.

The one-hour mingling is essential before a sit-down dinner so that all the guests can talk to each other. Once at the table, they'll only be able to talk to the right or to the left.

Take it from Eve:

Too much food is always better than too little, especially if you enjoy leftovers as we do.

Take it from Eve:

Be sure the lighting is flattering to the girls because if they "feel" beautiful, they will then be gracious and flattering to the men—and then everyone will have a ball.

CHEER UP THE BLUE BLUE *BLUES*

A girl I know describes it as feeling *utchy*. I think of it as feeling "just like a lump!"

Sometimes, it's the kind of day when the toothpaste cap falls off the edge of the sink and you can't find it on the floor and when you stand up, you bang your head on the pipes. Sometimes, you can't even pick up the toothbrush. It's too heavy. Your arms weigh a ton. The coffee tastes like car grease. The morning mail is a conspiracy of bills.

Bill who? No joke. Feeling rotten is no joke. The danger, however, lies in not forcing yourself to make it into a joke—or anyway a wry and temporary experience.

We all know the Telephone Bore.

Telephone Bore: Hi.

Friend: How are you?

Telephone Bore: I feel like hell. Everything hurts, etc. . . . (for three-and-one-half hours).

My feeling is, don't be a Telephone Bore and, in fact, if one calls you, cut the conversation short. When a Telephone Bore says, "I know I must be boring you . . . ," I always say, "Yes, you are."

When a Telephone Bore goes past the five minutes I generously allot for moaning and groaning, I say, "I'm tired of talking to you. Goodbye."

The next time you feel yourself on the verge of a filibuster about your terrible life, remember how it feels to be on the listening end and cut it short.

Feeling blue is two-sided, a combination of self-hatred and self-love. To worry about yourself and your temporary lack of energy and enthusiasm is sensible. To wallow in a sea of miseries and self-pity is about as helpful as walking barefoot in a snowstorm.

When you feel down, there's only one direction to go. Up. Develop your own Pick-Me-Ups and Perk-Me-Ups.

Constructive self-improvement heads my list. Most "blues" come from a sudden lack of confidence, a feeling of growing older, of being less attractive, of "nobody loves me" including yourself. That's why you should do your hair or have it restyled. Or give yourself a facial. Or take a long, luxurious bath. Or, simply, lie down for fifteen minutes. Many women make it a point of honor to die on their feet. "What, me lie down during the day? Never!" The world's most interesting and energetic people including Churchill, Eleanor Roosevelt, and John F. Kennedy, all understood the value of catnaps or just stretching out on the horizontal with eyes closed or leafing through a magazine.

A friend of mine told me she discovered that when she felt like hiding under the bed, she realized she was breathing in a shallow way. "So I started to do a few deep-breathing exercises. The additional oxygen seemed to pick me up in seconds."

Find out your own trigger to blast you out of the doldrums and pull it when needed.

Pull the trigger on the Miseries.

Haul out an old album of snapshots that always make you feel good.

Have handy a book that, from experience, jostles your sluggish brain. A girl I know loves *Alice in Wonderland*. Another friend cracks up reading Groucho Marx's collection of letters. Another has an anthology of *New Yorker* cartoons that make her laugh. Some women read their children's letters from camp and have a giggle. Poetry, a favorite short story, a passage from the Bible, a philosophical essay—find what works for you.

My own continuing source of pleasure is Kahlil Gibran's *The Prophet*. It's like a magnificent painting. The more I look at it, the more I see and the more enjoyment I get.

When it comes to fighting the blues, the woman who keeps house is in worse shape than the one who goes to work. As housewife and mother, you have heavy responsibility but you have no boss during the day. If you goof off because you feel lumpish, there's no one to tell you to shape up. The career girl who wakes up feeling like an old galosh soon forgets all about it in the rush to get where she's going and do what she has to do.

You may say, "What are friends for if I can't complain to them?"

This is true to a point. Friends are to be used but not abused. If you're down with the flu or the cellar got flooded or the baby broke his arm or your husband got fired, you're entitled to make your friend a crying towel. But, if it reaches the point, where the sound of your voice on the phone sends a chill of dismay through her bones, you're going to find yourself with a trunk full of tear-stained tales and no audience.

Friends *are* for cheering you up. Shake the blues by having lunch with a friend, hitting the museums, having your palm read, taking in a movie, buying a hat, shopping for Christmas or birthdays early.

Keep a mental file on the things that snap you out of the droops.

A case in point is New York socialite, Jane Stern, a busy wife, mother, and chairman of the board of the New York Chapter of W.A.I.F. for which I work, too. Jane once told me that when her boys were young, she would forget about running the household for a few hours and take them for an unexpected treat such as a visit to the zoo or a ride on a pony cart. Other mothers restore their perspective by taking the kids on a boat ride or to the aquarium or a science museum.

One of my friends takes her brood to one of the big pet shops in downtown Manhattan to see exotic birds, fish and snakes you don't find in a neighborhood shop.

An impromptu excursion is a fun time for the kids and is often just the change of pace Mom needs to come out of herself.

Take it from Eve:

When you feel low, put on a glamorous face. Ruthlessly force yourself to make up your eyes, comb your hair beautifully, not just comb it, and put on one of your favorite outfits. Looking your best, you will not only begin to feel better about the person you see in the mirror, but when you leave the house, you will receive the gift of appreciation from the eyes of those who see you.

A writer I know calls it psychic energy. She says that when she takes the trouble to look her best, she can feel the admiring glances of people in the street or the supermarket or wherever.

"I don't mean that people are falling over in a faint at the sight of my gorgeousness. What I do mean is the passing glance, even out of the corner of the eye, transmits a fleeting approval of my hair or my outfit or my stockings—and this approval is a form of psychic energy that quite literally pays you back for taking the trouble to look nice."

Take it from Eve:

Bright colors cheer you up. That's why I like red hats—or any crazy hats—and yellow rain coats, bright blue scarves, plenty of orange, pink, and purple. Not all at the same time, of course.

Take it from Eve:

When you really have something to complain about, try to see the lighter side of it and make your monologue as funny as possible. What saves the world from total disaster is a sense of humor. Except for a death or a hideous disease, almost any burden can be lightened and made more bearable if taken with a grain of salty wit.

PERSONAL TRADEMARKS

Students frequently worry about having an "Identity Crisis." As technology spreads, the problems of expressing individuality increase. You don't want to look like you were stamped out by a cookie-cutter. You don't want to be one of the faceless masses of people who make little personal impact.

You do want to achieve a special flavor that marks you as unmistakably you and not "what's-her-name" or like that cigarette they call Whatchamacallit.

Think about having a personal trademark, a certain something that is specifically and delightfully yours and that people will remember and associate with you. Perhaps you already have a personal trademark but haven't learned to exploit it properly. There needn't be anything exotic about it. You don't have to wear crabgrass in your hair or carry a Dragon Lady cigarette holder to attract attention.

The idea of a personal trademark is to project a continuing personal statement about yourself. Freaky things like carrying a giant paper flower to a cocktail party are fun for the moment but are abandoned immediately after the party. This is not a trademark.

A trademark can be handkerchiefs such as those that singer Hildegarde is never without. When she was plain Grace Kelly, Princess Grace was known for her short, white kid gloves. Brigitte Bardot's eggbeater hairdo is an extreme example of instant identification. (She had a few other things, too, but the hair immediately told you she was Brigitte and not some other sex kitten.)

Hats are my trademark. I *love* them. I love everything about hats. I love to shop for them. I love to buy them. I love the feel of a hat on my head—even a bathing cap. In fact, there are some people I've known for years who've never seen me without a hat.

One time, when I was a guest on Virginia Graham's TV show, "Girl Talk," Virginia said, "Do you ever take off your hat even when you go to sleep?"

Another time, Warren and I were invited to have Thanksgiving dinner at Mr. and Mrs. George Skouras' house. I wore one of my wilder creations, a feathery blue helmet hat. Of course, Julia Skouras exclaimed over it. George graciously invited me to take off my hat and I continuously refused. I caught him glancing at me with disapproval during cocktails. When we sat down at the table, he couldn't contain himself any longer.

"What's the matter?" he asked, in a whisper that would crack paint off a wall. "Are you bald?"

Finally, he could stand it no longer. "You are a beautiful woman. I want to see how you look without that hat!" He knocked it off my head and sent it flying like a feathery bird across the room.

By this time, it was all a big joke so we laughed and the party went on. Evidently, he could relax only after assuring himself that I am not bald.

As a trademark, hats are ideal for me because I truly enjoy wearing them. I don't feel dressed without them during the day. On vacations and on weekends, I wear straw hats, denim hats, flower helmets in the sun; fur and felt and vinyl and anything else that's good protection and still fashionable in the winter.

This is my daytime look. At night, I never wear a hat, although often I will wear a wig or wiglet. For the opera or other elegant occasions, I usually wear an elaborate hairpiece with jewels or flowers worked into it.

I can recommend hats as a trademark which you can make personally your own. A young boy in our apartment house explained he's come to recognize me by a Garbo-style hat which I sometimes wear. I have it in many colors and fabrics. The style is becoming to me and I'm sure my friends always think of me in it.

How to Pick a Trademark

Analyze your personal tastes and see which one you might adopt and exaggerate as a dramatic expression of yourself. For instance, if you love to wear big, important *earrings*, this is a perfect trademark. Steve Allen's wife, actress Jayne Meadows, is known for her huge chandelier earrings. You can do the same, building up an interesting collection of unique pairs that capture attention and start conversations. You can be as zany or dramatic as you please.

"What's she going to dream up today?" those you know will anticipate.

Earrings can have enormous sentimental value. The pair you bought on your honeymoon, the ones Junior made for you at camp, those you made from your husband's cuff links. Making earrings is a cinch. All you need are the little backings for clip-on styles or the wires for pierced ears which are readily available in hobby shops. Or, with a pliers, you can easily take the backs off old earrings and put them on new ones.

In addition to the many beautiful earrings on sale in department stores and boutiques, there are magnificent antiques to be found in second-hand jewelry shops and even in an old family trunk.

Last New Year's Day, at the Guy Williams' New York penthouse apartment, we went to a Hangover Party where everyone was supposed to be recovering from New Year's Eve. The hostess was wearing something in her ears that looked familiar. When I got so I could focus, I realized she had foil-wrapped Alka-seltzers dangling on red ribbons from each ear lobe.

"For emergency," she quipped.

An earring nut altogether, she made what she called Beach Earrings last summer by flattening soda pop bottle caps with a hammer. For her husband's birthday party, she made earrings of paper coasters with her birthday boy's picture pasted in the middle.

Flowers are another good personal trademark. Use your

favorite posy—a daisy, a violet, a rose—on personal station-
ery, linens, gloves, and on patterns for scarves, blouses, linge-
rie. If you work, a bowl of Your Flowers, fresh or otherwise,
will refresh your eyes and personalize your desk in the eyes of
co-workers. At home, Your Flower makes the perfect centerpiece for parties as well as general household adornment.

Your Flower becomes a personal trademark, a glowing and
growing symbol of yourself to your husband, your family, and
your friends. "I always think of roses when I think of her!"

Eyeglasses work well as a trademark, especially if you have
to wear them and want to make it fun instead of a drag. As a
trademark, you can have a wardrobe of glasses in varying
frames for every occasion from a cross-country drive to a
night at the ballet. Sunglasses, with or without prescription
lenses, fit into this category.

In contrast to the Old Days when specs made us wrecks
and Dorothy Parker wrote about the problems of girls in
glasses never attracting any passes, eyeglasses are now rightly
called fashion accessories. The new shapes add to your face,
give your looks a new dimension, and provide a constant
source of variety. You can switch back and forth from quizzi-
cal Ben Franklins to innocent Twiggys to the sophisticated
wraparounds of Jackie Kennedy.

Or, you can always wear the same style and be known for
that, like Pauline Trigere and Fleur Cowels both of whom
prefer the blue-tinted lenses and simple, round shape.

Scarves work well as trademarks, too. Again, you must love
wearing them. One of my friends said she started to wear
scarves as a protection against sore throats. She became intrigued with them and is rarely seen without one. Her collec-

tion ranges from the twenty-five-cent red workman's hand-kerchiefs you buy in the dime store which she tucks inside turtle necks to the yard-square Pucci silk she bought two years ago in Rome "for half a year's salary."

To protect her throat, she originally copied the style of cowboys, folding the scarf into a triangle and tying the two ends high up behind her neck with the triangle in front, either tucked into a neckline or coat or left in full view. With a black knit shift, her enormous Pucci looks like a marvelous bib that reaches halfway to her waist.

Scarves have become a look that is distinctively hers.

My fashion assistant, Mary Ann Napoleon, loves scarves so much that she includes them as accessories in all of our fashion shows. It's reached the point where a co-worker re-marked, "Mary Ann wants every model on the runway to wear one, carry one—or eat one!"

Fragrance can be a wonderful trademark, but only if you are really devoted to one particular scent that instantly means you. If you do have one fragrance that pleases you and seems to express your personality, use it in all forms, including sachet for your personal linens, bath oil for the tub, and spray cologne to create a light, personalized mist about everything you do.

Choosing a *color* as a trademark is a bit self-limiting. Make it your trademark only if it seems to be that anyway. For instance, if you look great in Nile green or hot pink and you always wear it because it makes your skin glow and you never get tired of it, then it already is your trademark and all you have to do is dramatize the affinity.

"Orange is your color, Beulah!" If you're like Beulah, then

adjust your fashion thinking to include "your" color on a bigger scale than you may have previously. For instance, if orange is truly a knockout on you, then have an orange coat or an orange suit as a wardrobe basic. The backbone of your wardrobe doesn't have to be a sensible brown or gray. If orange is your color, then orange is a far more sensible choice.

Discussing this point with the wife of a young executive, I knew she would go far when she confided to me, "Whenever I go out to buy a basic black dress, it's always red."

Take it from Eve:

It's fun and rewarding to have a personal trademark. It can be rings, especially if you have pretty hands. It can be shoes, especially if you have good ankles. It can be a semi-precious stone such as amber or carnelian that you can collect without robbing a bank. It can be a monogram that appears discreetly on many of your possessions. These days, it can be boots— your collection ranging from evening boots in lace to leather ranch boots.

Take it from Eve:

A trade mark is something that expresses you physically as well as artistically. It's something you have with you all the time. Don't confuse a trademark with a hobby. It's better than a hobby. You can't carry fourteen thousand Ming Dynasty pencil sharpeners around with you all day.

Making your own greeting cards is a personal expression people will not only remember but expect. Your own original designs have an extra something that store-bought cards can never have. The annual Christmas card that Warren and I send out has become a seasonal event that all our friends count on with the same certainty that their children count on the arrival of Santa.

Hand-made birthday cards and congratulations on other occasions have grown into a trademark for me. I love making them and I hate to see a special moment in a friend's life go by without acknowledging it.

A trademark should be an integral part of a woman's feminine image. Look at it that way and others will, too.

On the Subject of Hair-Rollers

There is a prevailing myth that the woman who wears hair-rollers in the house is doomed to lose her husband and any future chance of love and happiness. I think it's time someone said, "This is ridiculous!"

Take it from Eve:

This is ridiculous! While I do feel personally offended at the sight of a sloppy female in wrinkled shorts, no makeup and ugly rollers inside a torn net, wheeling her cart at the supermarket, I think the whole business about rollers at home has been exaggerated to an extreme.

Take it from Eve:

Marriage is an intimate affair. If you're the wife and woman you should be to your husband, your occasional appearance in rollers won't make a bit of difference. In fact, he probably won't notice them. If he does, he knows their purpose is to get ready for a party or something special.

This is not to say you should wear rollers to the extent your husband won't recognize you when you take them out. It's just that the whole no-rollers cry has gotten out of hand.

Take it from Eve:

When a man complains about his wife's rollers, he's not really complaining about the rollers at all. He's unhappy about something else.

Take it from Eve!

Eve's Peeves

Beware the calculations of the meek, who gambled nothing,
Gave nothing and could never receive enough.

—*John Ciardi*

A beautiful woman is like a tapestry. There is the expert composition of form, color, and design that is easily apparent on the surface. But what makes a tapestry three-dimensional is the richness below the surface. In a woman this richness is her desire to share beauty and to welcome the eye of the beholder.

That's why nothing aggravates me more than a woman who has learned how to achieve a beautiful façade but who spoils the effect by exposing what goes on under the surface as not so beautiful. True beauty comes from an extravagance of spirit and enjoyment of life. There is no room for pettiness or unthinking stupidity.

Unfortunately, there are *certain* people who do *certain* things which react on my poor, sensitive nerves like chalk on a blackboard. Not that I'm going to mention any names. You *know* who you are or you will know when you read this chapter.

You probably have some peeves about me, too. However, this happens to be my book and I would like to hang a verbal half-Nelson on the following:

"I'd love to entertain at home, but I can't get the right help. So we take people out to a restaurant."

This little cookie has spent eight years and five fortunes of her husband's (or husbands') decorating "La" home. The closets are swollen with china, silver, and linens. But when her husband says they've got to take clients to dinner, she says, "Fine," and makes a reservation at a restaurant!

To my mind, the chief purpose of entertaining guests is to make them feel at home. I don't happen to live in a restaurant. Hospitality means welcoming people into your pleasant, comfortable establishment.

As for the "right help," have you ever tried to get a waiter to bring the salt when he didn't feel like it? Unless you are giving a large sit-down dinner, I think a hired butler or maid detract from the warmth and informality of a dinner party. It's much nicer to have your husband do the drinks and you toss the salad—while in the kitchen a hired hand washes dishes, watches the pots, and puts on the coffee at the right moment.

"That was before my time!" You know her and that malicious smirk on her face, the type who implies she was four years old when she had her first child. "You're showing your age!" she teases if you mention anyone who was around before Ann-Margaret.

The attractive woman is an informed woman with a wide range of interests and knowledge. Because I know the words to "Yankee Doodle," does that mean I'm Paul Revere's mother? I think it's great to know the words of the old Rodgers & Hart songs, to be able to talk about Teddy Roosevelt and Charles Dickens.

If that's dating me, I have a two-word reply, "Too bad!"

"This is last year's dress." Who asked? The Excuse-maker fishes for compliments and sympathy but only exasperates her friends. If you feel driven to let everyone know you're not

wearing a brand-new Norell, make capital of the fact. Make an asset of, "Isn't it wonderful? I haven't gained an ounce since last year."

Instead of crying over spilt milk, laugh it up. If the butcher sent the wrong meat, say, "This started off as Boeuf Stroganoff—but I'm not sure what it is now. The butcher sent something that looks like an elephant."

And, the next time I hear, "I can't do a thing with my hair," I'm going to say, "You're absolutely right, darling. You can't!"

The Heiress who says, "I inherited my grandfather's big nose!" She never says where she got that big mouth. It doesn't dawn on her to talk about the nice things she may have acquired from her forebears such as her grandmother's lovely eyes.

The Sponge Brain who says proudly, "My Allen does my thinking for me. He makes all the decisions." When he decides to leave her, she'll have something to say, and then there won't be anyone around to listen.

Medicare Momma who purrs, "We're not young anymore, are we, dear?" Speak for yourself, Grandma. Include me out of the old-age club. When I'm ready for shuffle-board and darts, I'll let you know.

"Oh, how I envy you!" She's supposed to be your chum but when something nice happens to you, she ladles on the envy, moaning and groaning, "Oh, how I envy you." This, she tells herself, makes you feel good.

It doesn't. At least, not me. Share my joy. Don't drown it in acid tears.

The only woman who ever gave birth to a baby, she starts every sentence, "That reminds me of when I was having

Marjorie." Marjorie is now 17 and a freshman at Sarah Law-rence. Her mother is still "reminded" of the birth by such obviously related things as Vietnam, income tax time and summer vacations.

"What's happening to the younger generation?" I'll tell you what's happening. Self-styled Youth Experts keep asking, "What's happening to the younger generation?" Leave them alone. They'll go down in history.

The Diet Masochist who keeps saying, between bites, "I really shouldn't. . . ." Throughout your dinner party, she paralyzes conversation with her dazzling predictions that she is going to skip dessert. Skipping town would suit her better. At dessert time, she changes her mind, "I really shouldn't but . . ." which gives us all a terrible shock. Later, she regales the coffee conversation with repeated reminders that "somebody twisted my arm." Also, "Please pass the mints."

The Marriage Expert who says, "We married too young." The only way to shut her up is to comment, "What a tragedy for your husband."

The Fiend Indeed. That's not a typographical error. I'm talking about the alleged friend of the lady who wears size 20. The Fiend Indeed pooh-poohs the mere mention of a diet, reassuring her blimpy companion, "You're not fat—you're *big* —and you're in perfect proportion!"

For what, a pup tent?

To someone who is thinking about plastic surgery for a large nose, friend Fiend assures, "Nobody notices your nose. Your personality is so good."

It's almost as if the Fiend wants her friends ugly and dowdy.

The Group Analyst tells how she "was the middle child and never got the attention the other children got!" Just because she got caught in the middle doesn't mean everyone she meets has to get caught in a muddle of psychoanalytical naïveté. Just because someone once got caught in a blizzard doesn't make him a weather expert.

Right?

Everybody together now, shout, *"Right!"*

Dial-a-Mother who calls home very two seconds to "see how the children are." She is relentless in her yen to prove to the world that she is a superb mother. Despite the fact that her kiddies are half-grown and there is a competent sitter who knows exactly where to reach Mom in an emergency, she has to jump up and down as if to say all the other mothers at the party are not as dedicated as she.

The Status-seeker who frets, "I don't know how we're going to manage two cars in a one-car garage!" You know she has two cars. She's told you eighty times. You may be able to shut her up by saying, "I don't know how you're going to manage to make conversation after you build a two-car garage. You won't have anything to talk about."

Mrs. Clean who innocently protests, "But what does the joke mean?" She's had a very sheltered life. From the sound of it, in some underground shelter. She's never heard a racy story in her entire life and nearly faints with outrage at the thought of anything sexier than a cup of hot milk.

However, she always listens very, very attentively.

Husband Heckler who begins every sentence, "He—" Her husband once had a name and it is likely he's sorry by now that he gave it to her. She never mentions his name, assuming we know who she means by "*He* doesn't give me enough money . . . ," "*He* doesn't know how to make friends . . . ," "*He* never does anything right. . . ."

She seems to think her friends get a kick out of hearing her kick the guts out of her husband. We're waiting for him to kick *her* out!

P.S. Since this is not a political message, I don't have to give equal time. You probably have plenty of peeves about me. If you do, don't send them to me. Write your own book.

Epilogue

Now that you've read my book, I would like to sum up what I believe really makes a woman beautiful.

A woman truly is more beautiful when she can give love and be loved.

So—to all the potentially beautiful women in the world—I WISH YOU LOVE!

E.N.